Richard H. Cartier
FGA, FCGMA

Professional Jewellery Appraising

Jewellery Valuation
Theory and Practice

Toronto, 2004

Edition
2

National Library of Canada Cataloguing in Publication

Cartier, Richard H., 1944-
        Professional jewellery appraising : jewellery valuation, theory
and practice / Richard H. Cartier.

Includes index.
ISBN 0-9735316-0-6

        1. Jewelry--Valuation. 2. Gems--Valuation. 3. Precious stones--
    Valuation. I. Title.

TS756.C37 2004   739.27'029   C2004-902504-X

Printed in Canada
Cover art: Richard H. Cartier
© Fischer Presses and Richard H. Cartier, 1996
© Richard H. Cartier, 2004
All rights reserved
Printed in Canada
Statutory Copies: Quebec and Ottawa, 1st Trimester 2004
ISBN 0-9735316-0-6

Preface to the Second Edition

Jewellery appraising is gradually evolving from art toward science and the changes make appraisals much more useful, understandable, and user-friendly for consumers and as well as other segments of society. This evolution is important for the entire jewellery industry as well as those in other fields (such as law enforcement, jurisprudence, charities, taxation, and insurance) who use appraisals for whatever purpose. The only people disadvantaged by rational changes are unscrupulous people who misuse questionable appraisals as selling tools, and the immoral or foolish people who produce inflated appraisals for the unscrupulous.

With jewellery appraisals, the evolution toward science allows all users to be much better served by an approach that is systematic rather than inspirational, by a perspective that leans more toward the objective rather than subjective, by content that is more rational than creative.

In analysing the appraising process and outlining content requirements for appraisals, this book offers direction in that evolution.

I recognise the undeniable advantages of this move toward science, but rather hope that the "art" in appraising is not completely lost in the transition. The higher the quality of a piece of jewellery, in terms of design and execution, the more firmly it belongs within the classification of art. It would seem beyond dispute that the visionary expression of art cannot be fully realised in the mundane cataloguing of science.

Measurement and analysis are important in an appraisal but so are vision and insight. I hope that artistic techniques can be used with scientific rigor, that substance can be presented with style. The professional appraisal should be based on scientific research and analysis, and artfully presented to preserve the mystique and art in the items described and valued.

Acknowledgments

This book could not have been written without the advice, encouragement, and assistance of many people to whom I would like to express sincere gratitude and appreciation. Those named below were of particular help in making this book a reality, and I apologise to those I have forgotten to mention. None of these people can be blamed for any errors or omissions because I did not always incorporate their suggestions or revisions.

My thanks go, in no particular order, to ... Harold Weinstein and Anne Neumann for my formative baptism of fire in the art of jewellery appraising; Maurine Charlton for reviewing early versions of the manuscript; James B. Nelson for discussions, explanations, and copies of literature on the subject of colour science; Anna Miller and John Sinkankas for advice and encouragement; Peter Buckie for some excellent pointed criticism of earlier manuscript content on price, cost, and value; Brian Dunn for reviewing some of the text and offering helpful comments; Philip Batchelor for international liaison work; Richard Drucker for advice, encouragement and permission to use and quote from the Gemworld Price Guide; Paul Korsten for helpful insights regarding mark-ups; Peter Herschman for raising some issues of tax rules and regulations; Jack Adams for insights about insurance; David Beach for review and helpful criticism about valuation levels and insurance replacement; Andrew Hajsaniuk for a careful critique of the manuscript and advice regarding legal matters; Dee Dee Cunningham for diligent review and criticism of later versions of the manuscript; Francine Payette for review and criticism of early content and for layout and editing of the first edition; and last but very far from least, my dear wife Elizabeth for exceptional patience and understanding as a "computer widow" while I spent long hours at the keyboard making seemingly endless revisions.

R. Cartier

October 1996

Introduction

This book was written to serve as a text in the study of jewellery appraising, a reference for the practising appraiser, and a source of information for the appraisal user.

There is a rich breadth of information on valuing particular categories of jewellery in other books about appraising that I have been able to acquire from various sources, but I have had difficulty reconciling my understanding with some of the jargon and many explanations that were offered regarding appraising theory and procedures.

I hope that this book will fill a gap in the literature on jewellery appraising by presenting appraising theory and procedures in a logical and meaningful way. This will better prepare the student and the practising appraiser to rationally think their way through any perilous, awkward, or unusual situations to appropriate, valid conclusions. It is also intended to provide the end user with information to judge between a superior and an inferior jewellery appraisal. The key to superior performance will always lie in being thorough at both main aspects of appraising: fully and accurately identifying each item, and establishing a realistic appropriate value.

The appraiser requires a wide spectrum of knowledge, skills, tools, and resources. My goal here is to shed some light on the subject for those learning about appraising, for those actively practising the appraising art, and for those using appraisals.

In some ways the appraiser may be seen as the conscience of the jewellery industry and the quality of the appraiser will hinge upon attitude and approach. In the same way that the industry would be better served by appraisers looking beyond liability to responsibility, it is hoped that appraisers will progress beyond truth to honesty and then beyond honesty to integrity.

Table of Contents

Appraising Theory

A jewellery appraisal[1] is an expert opinion that provides interested parties with important needed or desired information. The expertise required includes much more than knowledge of gems and jewellery. Based on experience, expertise must include insights and skills acquired through training and practice. Expertise includes comprehension, judgement, knowledge, and ability.

Basic appraising concepts

The expertise of the professional appraiser should be used with wisdom and integrity to provide expert advice that is both understandable and unambiguous to assist the non-expert in making decisions of consequence.

Appraise

Appraise: (verb) to judge identity quantity, quality, and worth of a thing.

Appraisal

Appraisal: (noun) an expert opinion of authenticity, design, composition, quality and value.

---

[1]In some English speaking parts of the world the term *valuation* is used as a synonym or substitute for *appraisal*. Whichever term is used, care must be taken to avoid excessive significance for monetary value at the expense of composition and quality considerations.

The most   )er document, but
the opinion co   ch as verbally, by
signs or, theo   .n expert opinion
constitutes an appraisal whether or not it is in writing. The vast majority
of appraisals will be embodied in an appraisal document which, whether on
paper or in electronic storage, is a de facto claim of expertise by the issuer
and a record of an expert opinion for a particular case.

The phrase *de facto claim of expertise means that the mere existence
of the appraisal document stands as proof that the person who issued the
appraisal* **claims to be an expert**. *That claim of expertise* **should** *be
based on a firm foundation of specialized training*, knowledge, experience,
and skill used with diligence and integrity.

Needs met by appraisals

Appraisals may satisfy a number of different needs including:
o   To identify an item to be insured.
o   The basis for calculating insurance premiums.
o   To establish a limit of insurance coverage.
o   The basis for settlement of a loss or damage claim.
o   As evidence in litigation.
o   To establish import duties, taxes, and/or penalties payable.
o   To re-identify jewellery (e.g. returning from abroad).
o   To establish the tax deduction for a donation.
o   To establish a capital gain or capital loss.
o   For probate (i.e. legal basis to settle an estate).
o   Property settlement in a divorce or end of a partnership.
o   To establish the collateral level for a loan.
o   To establish the reserve bid for jewellery at auction.
o   The basis of an asking price in resale of the article.
o   To satisfy curiosity regarding identity and value.

It has been widespread practice to use insurance appraisals as sales
tools to give prospective clients an indication of savings inherent in the
retailer's asking price. When this is done it is most often not appropriate

since, even if the appraisal is realistic, the valuation level is usually misrepresented (see fair market value p12 and appraisal for resale p45).

An appraisal is neither an estimate to replace nor an offer to purchase. It is a claim of expertise by the issuer and it is an official record of an expert opinion for a particular case.

Appraiser

> **Appraiser**[2] **:** (noun) an expert who produces an appraisal.

In most jurisdictions there are no defined legal requirements for jewellery appraisers. In this circumstance an appraiser could be anyone who claims to have particular expertise that they can use to judge qualities (i.e. evaluate) and perform valuations. In jurisdictions where there are legal definitions regarding jewellery appraising they tend to be exclusionary rather than approbatory, allowing the courts to exclude persons from doing appraising under specified circumstances without comprehensively defining all who may do appraising. A jewellery appraiser **should be** a knowledgeable expert with the training, ability, experience and resources to identify stones and other materials; grade diamonds, pearls, cultured pearls, coloured gems, and luxury synthetic stones; describe jewellery; research specialty items and various markets; deduce costs of materials, design and workmanship; understand mark-ups; and establish valuation levels. Appraisers in other fields will have their own relevant areas of specialized knowledge.

Description requirements

Many people believe that the most important component of an appraisal is the value. This is not true! Quite clearly the most important part of the appraisal is a complete and accurate description. The description must identify each item and justify the final conclusion as to value. Without a precise description the identity of the item cannot be verified and the validity of the valuation may be questioned because there

---

[2] In some English speaking parts of the world the term *valuer* is used as a synonym or substitute for *appraiser*. Whichever term is used, care must be taken to avoid excessive significance for monetary value at the expense of composition and quality considerations.

is no way to substantiate the conclusion of value. When a client insures jewellery, the final monetary value may establish the level of the insurance premiums but if the jewellery is damaged, lost, destroyed or stolen an explicit description will be of particular help in the process of restitution, replacement or repair.

If an insured suffers a loss, the description should provide sufficient detail to confirm that any replacement is indeed similar in all significant respects to the original. Should the item be recovered, the description should be sufficient to identify it.

The bottom line

There seems to be a general misunderstanding about price, cost, and value. Many people believe them to be equivalent. The common misconception seems to be that if the price or the cost of an item is fair then price and cost are equal to the value of the item.

Price, cost, and value

Price, cost, and value are really three quite different concepts. Each is a quantitative statement about the referenced subject.

Price

> **Price**: (noun) the consideration (usually monetary) asked for a product or service

Prior to the final conclusion of a sale the price is more or less negotiable. For this reason price may be of different types. Which type comes first depends upon who initiates the negotiations. Asking price is the offer to sell. Bid price is the offer to purchase. Agreed price is the conclusion of negotiations. How the term is used will very often indicate which type of price is meant and if it were unclear from the context, then asking price would usually be inferred.

A customer may make an offer that, if accepted, becomes an agreed price but is still not the selling price (buyer's cost) until the article is **fully paid for and delivery accepted**. Even if a deposit is made after an agreed price, this is still not the cost until the article is fully paid for because the sale may still fall through with the deposit being forfeited.

Cost

> **Cost**: (noun) the consideration (usually monetary) paid for a product or service.

The cost is set when an item is actually sold. The figure on a price tag is only the asking price. The tagged price will become the cost (selling price) only when a customer pays for and accepts the article in exchange for his payment. Selling price and cost refer to the same amount, *selling price* being from the point of view of the vendor and *cost* being from the point of view of the purchaser. From the point of view of a third party the term **cost** is preferred to the term *selling price* because it cannot be confused with bid price or asking price.

In a broader context there can be various types of cost. For the sake of consistency throughout this book we will be equating cost with selling price. In the case of an item sold at auction, for example, *cost* as it is used in this book (i.e. cost = cost price = selling price) would be the hammer price excluding any surcharge by the auctioneer. Surcharge included cost could be increased by payment of taxes. Tax included cost could again be increased by freight or delivery charges as well as insurance. Other expenses such as those associated with the fees and expenses of a paid purchaser could further increase the delivered cost.

Value

> **Value**: (noun) a quantitative statement of the (usually monetary) significance or desirability (the perceived worth) of a specified subject (usually a product or service) **to** a defined purchaser **from** a defined vendor in particular **circumstances** at a specified **time** with both parties having reasonable **knowledge** of all relevant facts.

In appraising we are particularly concerned with the concept of value, for it is value about which we must formulate an opinion. To do so we may consider costs and/or prices but the appraised value will be our perception of worth at a certain time, in a particular circumstance, for a definable hypothetical purchaser from a definable hypothetical vendor.

The only time value equates with cost is when the buyer, the seller, the circumstances and the time, as well as the knowledge of the principals, are in accord with the defined value. If someone buys an interestingly cut amethyst from a lapidary and sells it to a retailer who sets it in a piece of jewellery that is then sold to a satisfied consumer, what would be the value of the stone? If everyone was happy at each of the transactions then there are three values, one at each time and for each pair of principals. If the new owner then has the jewellery appraised and the appraiser correctly identifies the stone as a violet scapolite, the costs in each of the earlier sales are entirely unrelated to value because one or more of the principals did not possess knowledge of the relevant fact of the stone's correct identification. If the final owner does not seek to have the transaction revoked on the grounds of misidentification or misrepresentation, the transactions were valid legal sales. However, the costs in these legal sales were not related to value.

In practice a precise figure of value is rarely immediately available and the appraiser must establish a defensible hypothetical value. The value of an article is its perceived worth and that perception can change dramatically depending on point of view. What the value on an appraisal should be depends on the valuation date, who the appraisal is for, the kind of article being appraised, why the appraisal is sought and how it will be used.

Why, for what, how, and at how much?

In the 1990's a number of American books and courses were using the terms *purpose, function,* and *application with significantly different meanings than those given for them here. Those who used these words in unusual ways may have considered the words as jargon* developed particularly for the field of appraising.

Specialized fields can have their own internal jargon wherein words are given special meanings markedly different from their meaning in day-to-day use. An example of this is the word **form**, which has a very narrow meaning in crystallography. Novice students of crystallography may misunderstand **form** to mean shape, but it is a jargon label in this field that represents an important concept (the complete assemblage of all faces required by the symmetry when one face is given) that is so narrow in meaning as to not have a label in ordinary conversation outside the specialized field. In this example the jargon helps to clarify basic concepts.

Jargon has also been used for other purposes, such as comfortable communication with peers in a field, coded communication to limit information to those in the specialized field, or simply as bafflegab to impress people outside the specialized field.

R. S. Joseph in **Effective Insurance Appraising** (1996) defines **purpose** as *"kind of value" and* **function as** *"what the appraisal will be used for"* in conformity with the *1990's American jargon* trend. These definitions seem to contradict the usual day-to-day meaning of these words.

Purpose is cerebral in nature, having a great deal to do with intention. More than anything else it has to do with striving toward a particular end. Whatever the context, purpose is (or is centred upon) the <u>objective</u> or thing intended. The sentence "What is your purpose in seeking this appraisal?" would be a self-explanatory context using the word **purpose** appropriately, as understood in ordinary every-day use.

Function, on the other hand, is the <u>mode of action </u>by which something fulfils a purpose. It is the way in which something does its job.

Usually *purpose* answers the question "What is the objective?" and function answers the question "How?" in normal conversation.

For the concept *"what the appraisal will be used for"* it seems apparent that "application" would be an appropriate term. See the later section entitled **Valuation levels** for this author's explanation of *"kind of value"*.

There is no necessity for especially re-defining words in an unusual way as jargon to clarify concepts when the concepts exist in every-day conversation with ordinary meanings for ordinary words.

There can be no quarrel with those who have internalized such jargon and are comfortable using it to communicate with peers, provided the jargon is not misused. It is suggested that jargon is being misused when it serves to disguise or hide information, or when it is mere puffery.

It is doubtful if using jargon to disguise information from those outside the field is efficacious, the consequence of deliberately misleading a client may be problematic. Some might see an advantage in jargon as bafflegab to impress people outside the appraising field, but it would undoubtedly be better to provide the client with useful understandable information.

Purpose

Purpose: (noun) the intention of the client seeking to commission an appraisal, or the intention of anyone who offers an appraisal as evidence, or the intention of anyone who relies upon the content of an appraisal to arrive at a decision to take an action of consequence.

When an appraisal is commissioned the client seeks the expert opinion with a particular intent. The intention of the client is the purpose, the reason why the appraisal is wanted. The purpose sets what type of appraisal is required and will be one of the major factors in establishing the appropriate valuation level. "For insurance" is one common purpose that is often specified.

Function

Function: (noun) the way by which an appraisal (or part of an appraisal) fulfils a purpose (The mode of action in fulfilling a purpose).

From the purpose, the function(s) of the appraisal can be ascertained. The appraisal can then be tailored to adequately perform the required functions.

An appraisal for insurance, for example, serves four main functions:
o To identify the item that is subject to being insured, the description in the appraisal must be accurate and complete.

- As the basis for calculating insurance premiums the appraisal must offer a value that is not so high as to have the client paying too much for insurance coverage, particularly if the insurance company's liability in case of a loss is limited to the **lesser** of the cost of replacement or the stated value for insurance.

- As the basis for establishing a limit of insurance coverage the appraisal must offer a value that is not so low as to limit replacement possibilities any more than the insured or insurer would find acceptable.

- As the basis for settlement of a loss or damage claim the description in the appraisal is of paramount importance in ensuring that any replacement is indeed similar in all significant respects to the lost item.

Other functions, such as providing information of interest to the owner, would be ancillary to these main functions.

Assigned use

> **Assigned use**: (noun) the principal intended application for the appraisal as specified by the appraiser within the appraisal document.

The assigned use may be specified within the name of the type of appraisal that has been produced, in the body of the appraisal itself, or in a separate disclosure statement which is part of the appraisal document. It indicates the perspective that was taken by the appraiser in analysing the item(s) and in formulating the expert opinion. It also provides direction to the end-user of the appraisal as to the most appropriate application of the expert advice embodied in the appraisal document.

Application

> **Application**: (noun) The use to which an appraisal is put.

Some applications outside the scope of the assigned use may be quite valid. For example an appraisal for insurance may validly serve to re-identify articles taken on holiday and carried back home from abroad when possible import duties or taxes could be charged on a new imported item. For this application value is not at issue, it is the description that serves the required function. The detailed description identifies the item to prove previous existence and imply prior ownership.

Other applications outside the scope of the assigned use are not valid. For example, an appraisal for probate should never be used as the basis for insurance, nor should an insurance appraisal serve as the negotiation basis on the resale of an item. In these instances **value is at issue** and the valuation level for each case is not appropriate.

Valuation levels[3]

It is rather humbling to recollect moments of arrogant foolishness. I remember once feeling rather smug about my "superior" understanding of appraisal theory when discussing the concept of value with another appraiser. We had agreed that it would not be appropriate for anyone to provide "investment value" appraisals (not even considering that it would be foolish to accept any responsibility for someone else's future capital gain). He pronounced that there was only one legitimate valuation level, *retail replacement value. I was quick to point out his oversight that a probate* appraisal could not be at that same level. I then made my own equally incorrect pronouncement that there were two valuation levels, retail replacement value and probate value. As will be seen below, there are a multitude of possible valuation levels, and probate is a type of appraisal that may have differing valuation levels depending upon jurisdiction.

The appropriate valuation level for each appraisal will depend upon who the appraisal is for and the circumstances and purpose of the appraisal. Most appraisals for insurance will be at retail replacement value, although replacement-reproduction value or duplication value are other options

---

[3] NOTE: This information is not legal opinion or legal advice. Reading, viewing, or receiving it does not create or constitute an attorney-client relationship. To the best of the author's knowledge and belief references herein to legislation, tax rules, administrative practices, and/ or jurisprudence were up to date and correct at the time of writing, but laws, rules, practices, and legal rulings are continuously evolving. It is recommended that for cases having tax consequences, or of particular legal consequence, you consult with an accountant or lawyer of appropriate specialization for up to date information and advice. It is further suggested that you make a point of offering this same recommendation to any client you advise.

depending upon the client's requirements, details of the insurance contract, and the kind of article. "Wholesale tax-included" could be an appropriate valuation level if the client is someone in the industry with access to true wholesale who wants to insure personal jewellery. Tax-included in this case refers to the hidden Federal Excise Tax, not retail sales taxes. The insurance broker and the underwriter will then decide whether they want to handle the coverage and at what cost.

Be sure to have a clear understanding of fair market value. It is often defined and required by law, particularly for appraisals that have tax consequences (see probate appraisal p41).

The following definitions and explanations of valuation levels are generally set out in ascending order of magnitude with forced sale value being the lowest and duplication value being the highest for most articles of unknown provenance.

Forced sale value

> **Forced sale value**: (noun) what an article would sell for in circumstances requiring disposal within a specified time frame or by a particular date.

At forced sale value the vendor is compelled to convert the property into cash on or before a specific date. If a liquidation date is not specified a relatively short time limit is assumed, such as forty-eight hours or within a week. When there is a longer lead-time, the actual required liquidation date or the duration of time the goods are to be exposed for sale should be specified.

Forced sale value will be the lowest of the possible appraised values. It is the minimum amount that the owner should reasonably expect to receive when asking for bids to purchase the article for immediate cash. The hypothetical prospective purchaser will formulate a bid based on the assumption that the hypothetical vendor must accept one of the offers tendered at the same time as his and will not have opportunity to seek better offers at another time or within another venue. For jewellery of modern manufacture forced sale value could be discounted scrap value on the metal plus a fraction of the wholesale cost of the stones. For collectibles or antiques it might be what a used-goods dealer or antique dealer would consider a good buy to put into stock. Forced sale value will always be near the minimum it would fetch upon disposal.

Liquidation value

Liquidation value: (noun) what an article would sell for in circumstances requiring disposal without specific time or geographic constraints.

Liquidation value may be equal to, but more likely is somewhat higher than, the forced sale value. The hypothetical prospective purchaser will formulate a bid based on the assumption that the hypothetical vendor will have the option to decline all offers and seek better offers at another time (such as next month, or in two years) and/or within a wider marketplace (such as New York, London, Toronto, Tokyo, or Kuwait).

For collectibles or antiques it could be what a used goods dealer or antique dealer might pay in purchasing such an article to fill an inventory gap.

Liquidation value (compared to forced sale value) should be nearer to the maximum amount that can reasonably be expected to be realised upon disposal of the article. In cases with tax consequences, such as under the Canadian Cultural Property Export and Import Act where capital gains exemptions could be granted, this equates with "fair cash offer".

Fair market value

Fair market value: (noun) the price at which property would change hands between a willing vendor and a willing purchaser, without any premium, discount or price reduction, within a marketplace in which such property is most commonly sold, both parties having reasonable knowledge of all relevant facts and neither being under compulsion to buy or sell.

In theory, fair market value would be the mode price at which an article sells (i.e. the most commonly occurring ignoring extreme highs and lows, see **comparing numbers** p28). Some courts have accepted definitions that specify "the highest price"[4] but this could be misunderstood (by someone overlooking the requirement that the parties be prudent) to be an inappropriate invitation for inflated valuation, so this point is addressed in the definition by the phrase "without any premium, discount or price reduction". Definitions of fair market value that specify "retail" should refer only to property that, in its appraised condition, is generally obtained by the public in the retail marketplace[5]. Items usually not sold at retail would have to be considered within a different marketplace.

This is the **only** valuation level appropriate to show how much saving is achieved at a discounted asking price.

Only for unworn new jewellery should the fair market value be based on the retail price of new merchandise. This valuation level, however, is seldom asked for with an unworn new article. For used articles the fair market value should be based on the price of similar goods in the appropriate secondary market such as an estate department, used goods retailer or auction.

Fair market value of cut gemstones that are not set requires understanding the market. There have been problems internationally with boiler room type sales of loose gemstones "as investments". The stones are often accompanied by "certificates" that supposedly indicate the

---

[4] "The highest price, expressed in terms of money or money's worth, obtainable in an open and unrestricted market between informed and prudent parties, neither party being under compulsion to transact."
  Friedberg vs. The Queen [Dominion Tax Cases Court Decisions - Cited 89 DTC, copyright 1989, CCH Canada Limited]
[5] In the United States of America the Department of Treasury, in reference to estate (i.e. probate) evaluations, defines fair market value as "...the price at which the property would change hands between a willing buyer and a willing seller, neither being under any compulsion to buy or sell and both having reasonable knowledge of relevant facts. The fair market value of a particular item of property included in the decedent's gross estate is not to be determined by a forced sale price. Nor is the fair market value of an item of property to be determined by the sale price of the item in a market other than that in which such item is most commonly sold to the public, taking into account the location of the item wherever appropriate. Thus, in the case of an item of property includible in the decedent's gross estate, which is generally obtained by the public in the retail market, the fair market value of such an item of property is the price at which the item or a comparable item would be sold at retail." [**Treasury Regulation** 20.23031(b)]

qualities of the stones they describe. Even when certificates are reasonably accurate (which is rare) the "investor" finds that liquidation is a problem because there is no marketplace that comes close to meeting his expectation of return on investment.

If commissioned to appraise such stones, it would be wise to start with a consultation with the client to explain a few "facts of life". If you accept a commission to appraise un-mounted stones, avoid unnecessary jeopardy by declining to use an inappropriate valuation level. There would be no profit in becoming the defendant in a third-party litigation for damages. The reason "certificates" rather than appraisals originally accompanied such stones is that the issuer of the paper did not want any responsibility related to value.

To illustrate the point, several years ago I was commissioned by Revenue Canada to appraise a large number of loose gemstones that had been purchased by someone "as an investment" and then partly liquidated at a loss and partly disbursed to members of the family or otherwise disposed of and written off as a business loss. The income tax department, suspicious of the size of the claimed loss, wanted me to provide a "fair market value" for the stones. They seemed to expect a value near retail, which would have increased revenues into our government's tax coffers. The appropriate valuation level could only be established after formulating a clear understanding of both the gemstone marketplace and the concept of fair market value.

The most common marketplace for the majority of unset gems (other than finished art objects not normally set into jewellery) would be a stone dealer selling to manufacturers or retailers. The most frequently encountered wholesale gemstone transaction in which single, matched pairs, or matched sets of loose gemstones are marketed is sale by memorandum: the price a dealer would ask if sending the stone(s) out on an approval memorandum to a jeweller or manufacturer ("on appro" or "on memo"). This is the highest wholesale price because the jeweller does not actually buy the stone(s) but rather sells the stone(s) while acting as an agent for the stone dealer and does not have to pay for the stone until after it is sold. Fair market value for unset gemstones would be based on this wholesale memorandum price, although some circumstances may require "retail fair market value" (see donation appraisal p42).

Full fair value

Full fair value: (noun) The full price of an item, service, or privilege when it is sold with the vendor not suffering a loss.

When an item, service, or privilege is sold or distributed at a loss for the purpose of advertising (not a liquidation or sell-out "clearance") this would be termed a promotional distribution and the definition of full fair value would be as follows:

The price paid or cost incurred by a promotional distributor to obtain or manufacture a tangible property or to provide a taxable service; or, in respect of an admission, the price paid by the promotional distributor for the admission or, if the place of amusement is owned or operated by the promotional distributor, the normal and usual price charged for admission. In cases where there is a promotional distribution of a product, service, or admission to a place of amusement which would be subject to retail sales tax, the taxing authority may require that the tax be paid on the basis of this **full fair value** even though the promotional distributor may be giving away the product, service, or admission or may be selling it at a loss. If the promotional product, service, or admission is being given away the distributor must pay all the tax on the **full fair value.** If a reduced fee is being paid then tax is payable by the purchaser based upon that fee paid and the distributor is responsible to pay tax on the difference between the promotional fee paid by the customer and the **full fair value** so that the taxation authority receives the full amount of tax it otherwise would have received in a sale that was not a promotion or loss-leader.

Replacement/reproduction value

Replacement/reproduction value: (noun) what it might cost to have the article reproduced or replaced through an insurance replacement specialist.

This value assumes that the insurer (not the insured) will choose the vendor of the replacement article or any repair work and may choose to use unspecified or anonymous craftsmen. Whenever it is relevant, the appraiser (and the vendor or purchaser of any replacement or reproduction) should understand the issue of patents and abide by patent regulations. If the appraised item carries a design patent or if any component or part of an appraised item carries either a design patent or a function patent the appraisal assumptions must include an appropriately licensed supplier. There is further discussion about patents under the later heading of Duplication value.

This is the appropriate valuation level for a client whose insurance company, in the event of a loss, will provide the lowest cost replacement article available that meets or exceeds the description of the insured item in the appraisal. Most insurance companies would be flexible enough to allow a claimant to choose the supplier of a replacement item provided that the cost is comparable (not necessarily equal) to their lowest quoted cost.

It would be appropriate for an offer to replace, with a specified time limit on that offer, to accompany an appraisal at this valuation level. The document might have wording such as *"The* $\alpha \backslash \Omega$ *Jewellery Services Company Limited offers to reproduce or replace the item at the appraised value. This offer is valid for ninety days from the date of valuation."* on an enclosure with or included on the appraisal document. It should be clearly understood, however, that the offer to replace is entirely separate from the appraisal. The time limit relates only to the offer to replace and **not** to the appraisal **contents**. Even if the offer-to-replace time limit is specified within the appraisal document, the appraiser could be held liable for any errors or omissions beyond that time limit to the same extent as would apply to the contents of an appraisal not connected to any statement of time limit.

Clients should be advised to expect that replacement options would be limited by having articles insured at this valuation level. Frequent re-valuation would be strongly recommended to avoid becoming under-insured. Before deciding to use this valuation level, the client should consider that any potential saving in premiums would be offset to some extent, and perhaps more than offset, by the increased cost of more frequent valuations.

Most jewellery will have a retail replacement value that is higher than replacement/reproduction value.

Retail replacement value

> **Retail replacement value**: (noun) What a comparable article might realistically retail for without discounts from a jewellery retailer who sells like articles.

For appropriate articles this may alternatively be termed *retail antique value.* It is not what a retailer might charge to replace or duplicate a lost item, but rather, the price the hypothetical retailer would put on the item if he happened to have it in his stock.

Retail replacement value most often serves as the basis for insuring an article. It may be the actual cost of the article provided that the price was in no way discounted. Alternatively, it may be an opinion of what an identical or comparable article might sell for without discounts. If the article is replaceable with similar jewellery of modern manufacture then replacement with a comparable new (rather than used) article is usually assumed. This assumption does not apply to vintage or antique pieces and requires that any wear-and-tear on the article must not exceed what would be normal or typical of like items that are worn regularly.

That replacement of lost jewellery should be with new unworn jewellery may at first seem of questionable propriety. When an insured suffers a loss the insurer is obliged to re-establish the situation that existed before the loss occurred. The insurer is not obliged, however, to put the insured into an improved situation. If a three-year-old car were stolen, the insurance company would not buy the insured a new car, but will provide a similar make and model (i.e. a used three year old vehicle).

A jewellery article may cost as much as a car but if a ten year old ring is stolen the insurance company replaces it with a brand new ring. There are a few reasons for this. First, there is high intrinsic value in the component materials in jewellery so it does not depreciate in value the way the car does. Second, style, design and features do not as a matter of course change annually with jewellery the way they do in automobiles so jewellery is (usually) less "dated" than an automobile. Third, it is easier to find or make new jewellery to match the description of a lost item than it would be to find a closely matching used item. Finally, and some might say most importantly, there is the symbolism and mystique of gems and jewellery. Many women would vigorously object to, and some would be quite horrified at the thought of, wearing a used engagement ring from a failed marriage in place of their original engagement ring.

Not every buyer is a bargain hunter and retail replacement value does not assume the hypothetical purchaser has the time or inclination to comparison shop for a discount. Retail replacement value will, therefore, indicate the high end of retail. When someone pays insurance premiums on this higher value the insurer should be accepting a higher risk for the higher premium. The insured should not be burdened with the requirement to expend time or energy in bargain hunting when they suffer a loss. This does not mean, however, that it is a fictitious artificially high amount from which a retailer can discount and still make a normal mark-up. Even though it is at the high end of retail it must be a realistic retail value and should be defensible as such.

This is the appropriate valuation level at which to insure jewellery when the insurance policy allows someone who has suffered a loss while insured to choose who will undertake the replacement (within the coverage limits established by the appraisal). From the retail customer's point of view, he can expect that replacement can be undertaken by his own jeweller whom he has come to know and trust with price being no object up to the limit of the coverage for which he has paid.

NOTE: Many insurance policies will limit the liability of the insurer to the lowest replacement or repair cost they can negotiate, which leaves the insured in the position of not being able to freely choose who does replacement work even though the cost of the insurance coverage was based on a higher valuation. This may upset some clients who see this as unfair. When the liability of the insurance company is limited to whatever replacement cost the company can negotiate, the client may request a lower valuation (see Replacement/reproduction value p15).

The underwriter works for the insurance company, not the client. He decides whether or not it is in the insurance company's interest to accept a specified risk. If the risk to the company is too great the underwriter will decline coverage; if the client offers to pay higher than necessary premiums, the underwriter may agree that the risk to the company is acceptable, and the insurance company pockets high premiums.

With liability limited at an amount below the coverage paid for, the client may not want to accept retail replacement value as the basis for insuring the article. Most clients do not understand that insurance coverage may be limited to less than the appraised value and that there are other valuation levels.

If the appraisal document or cover sheet does not offer definitions or explanations of valuation levels, an appraisal at retail replacement value should include in the declaration of costing assumptions a statement to the effect that the appraisal assumes that any replacement will be by the client's choice of retailers (see the example in the appendix).

Duplication value

> **Duplication value**: (noun) What it might cost to have a new item constructed which is as exact a duplicate of the item as can be produced in comparable or identical materials, design, and workmanship.

This could be the part-set value of one article from a set, the valuation for insurance of an item that is not readily replaceable on the basis of having constructed a new article that matches the specified item as nearly as possible, or the valuation for insurance of an item on the basis of duplication of the item by the original designer/craftsman. For example, if the owner of an antique item particularly likes specific design details of a piece and has no concern whatever for the antique status, duplication value could be an appropriate basis for that client to seek insurance coverage.

Whatever specification sets duplication value as different from retail replacement value or from replacement/reproduction value should be noted on the appraisal document. With the cited example the document might specify, "In the event of a loss the client requires that any replacement be as exact a duplicate as can be produced by modern manufacture."

Whenever there is a requirement for duplication of a piece of jewellery due consideration must be given to the issue of patents.

Patents[6]

Our society recognises that new and original ideas provide society with opportunity for advancement and improvement. It is generally agreed that individuals who first formulate a new idea should be recompensed with particular entitlements for making their idea available to the rest of society, so the concept of intellectual property rights has evolved.

Within the overall concept of intellectual property, copyrights and trademarks cover original ideas that might be under the general category of communicating and marketing. Patents cover original ideas for physical objects.

The basic idea of a patent is to add information to the available public knowledge about things that can be manufactured or produced while rewarding the originator of an ingenious and/or novel idea for making the idea public by recognising him as the inventor and granting him a time-limited exclusive right to make, use, and sell the invention or license others to do so. This increase in public knowledge fuels technological advancement and helps improve the general economy and standard of living in our industrialised society.

There are two types of patents relevant to the field of gems and jewellery.

Design patents are granted in some jurisdictions for original ornamental designs. Items covered by a design patent are protected on the basis of their appearance and unlicensed individuals or companies are prohibited from producing, using, or selling similar items that look like the item protected by the patent. The princess cut and the quadrillion cut (p194) are examples of similar appearing cuts, but the princess cut is not patented while the quadrillion cut is design patented in addition to having the name trademarked.

Design patents may be more related to fashion than to function, and a similar object with a minor but noticeably different design feature may be adjudged to not infringe on a design patent. The noticeably smaller table

[6] NOTE: This information is not legal opinion or legal advice. Reading, viewing, or receiving it does not create or constitute an attorney-client relationship.

of the princess cut should be sufficient to distinguish it from the very large table of the patented quadrillion cut, for example. When the appraiser names styles of cut of gemstones they should be accurately reported with the knowledge of which styles are design patented.

A utility patent (which is the type most often thought of when patents are discussed, and are a type issued in all jurisdictions) is granted for an original and useful machine, manufacture, process, or composition of matter, or for a useful improvement thereof. Connectors and fasteners are the type of thing to which utility patents can apply. The "easy-loc" clasp is an example of a utility patent in jewellery.

With a utility patent, function is far more at issue than fashion so major and even overwhelmingly obvious ornamental design differences may be adjudged as irrelevant to a claimed infringement of a utility patent. In such a case the claim of the patent holder would be upheld.

Whenever it is relevant, the appraiser (and the vendor or purchaser of any duplicate item) should understand the issue of patents and abide by patent regulations. If the appraised item carries a design patent or if any component or part of an appraised item carries either a design patent or a function patent, the appraisal assumptions must include an appropriately licensed supplier and it should be clearly understood that duplication of the item can only be made by the patent holder, or a licensee, or by acquiring the patented part through a licensed supplier.

Declared value for insurance

Declared value: (noun) The amount of money that would be appropriate compensation for complete loss of an insured article.

If accepted as the basis for insurance coverage, the declared value for insurance becomes the agreed cash value.

The most usual circumstance when this would be the appropriate valuation level is if all items potentially comparable to the article have such significant or consequential differences that the only approach suitable for establishing the value is to consider how much this article itself might realise if offered for sale on the open market.

The article is not readily replaceable so insurance cannot be undertaken on the basis of replacement. Coverage then becomes "value insurance" which would presume monetary compensation for a loss rather than replacement.

In such cases the opinion of value by the expert, arrived at by hypothesising the sale of the item itself with a duly defined vendor and purchaser, becomes a declared value by the client when he submits the appraisal as the basis for insuring the item. This declared value becomes an agreed value when the insurance company accepts to underwrite the policy in the full knowledge that the item is not readily replaceable.

The phrase "not readily replaceable" must not be casually used, and would be completely misused in referring to an article when the name of the valuation level for that article includes the word "replacement"!

Special values

Special value: (noun) a level of value specific to the individual case as defined within the appraisal document.

Special values may be required under special circumstances.

Values such as **dealer cost** (i.e. what a **wholesale** dealer might pay to buy stock), **wholesale on license** (i.e. what a manufacturer licensed to collect hidden taxes might pay to buy stock), **wholesale tax-included** (i.e. what a retailer might pay, including hidden taxes, to buy stock), or **wholesale antique value** (i.e. what one antique dealer might pay another antique dealer to buy stock) will very rarely be the valuation level required in an appraisal. When such valuation levels are used the appraiser should ensure that the people receiving his appraisal report have access to such articles at the specified level and/or clearly understand the significance of the valuation level.

It is perfectly appropriate to define a special valuation level to meet particular needs of a special case. In defining other valuation levels consider the relevant time, vendor, purchaser, and circumstances with a legally allowed transaction in a legitimate marketplace.

Actual cash value

> **Actual cash value**: (noun) The amount of money calculated to be suitable for settlement of an insurance loss

"Actual cash value" is a term used by insurance companies and is not a value in the sense of envisioning a vendor and purchaser for the item. It is a method of calculating a cash settlement in the event of a loss and can only apply to depreciable property. The adjuster starts with the cost of a new replacement item and deducts depreciation according to the category of item as set out in charts established for this purpose indicating average life expectancy.

The term "actual cash value" and this approach to settlement of a claim is peculiar to items with a limited life span and is seldom used when the lost item is jewellery. Some jewellery items would actually appreciate in their commercial value rather than depreciate. Other items, which would have no commercial value other than as scrap (a worn wedding band, for example), may have a mystique for which the concept of depreciation would be entirely inappropriate.

The valuation level that most closely corresponds to this "actual cash value" would be fair market value.

Fictitious values

FICTITIOUS VALUATION LEVELS such as "investment value" or "wholesale-to-the-public" must never be condoned. Such an appraisal would be a complete misrepresentation of value, implying a market that does not legitimately exist. They are not defensible and could be considered fraudulent.

Valuation approaches

There are essentially three different approaches one can adopt in determining value: the costing approach, market data comparison, and the income approach. The first two of these approaches are of particular relevance to gems and jewellery.

Costing approach

The largest proportion of jewellery submitted for appraisal is of relatively modern manufacture and is more or less readily replaceable with comparable new jewellery. For such items the most common marketplace would obviously be a jewellery store, and it would be appropriate to use the ***costing approach*** to establish value. This approach is based on the valuer's perception of how much it would cost to produce the item in the current market with similar design, authenticity, qualities and craftsmanship. The cost of each component is analysed separately and hidden taxes and mark-ups are factored in to arrive at the appraised value.

Hidden taxes are any taxes that are included in the price of an article without the knowledge of the final consumer. For example a manufacturing tax or a luxury tax, which adds to the cost of an article before it reaches the retail sales point, is a hidden tax. In Canada the Federal Excise Tax is now 10 percent. Although it is hidden, it must be included in value determination where relevant.

The Canadian federal goods and services tax (GST), the provincial sales tax, or the British value added tax (VAT) is a retail sales tax that is not hidden from the consumer. Their inclusion in the opinion of value is optional. The appraisal document should specify whether the valuation includes or excludes any relevant retail sales taxes. If it is desired to include retail sales taxes in the report this can be done in three different ways. The taxes may be named with their percentages mentioned and specified as included. The taxes may be itemized and appended to the sales-tax-excluded appraised value. As an alternative, separate tax-excluded and tax-included values may be given. The rationale for this is that the appraisal can continue to be valid over a period when taxation levels change, or from one place to another where retail sales taxes may differ. The choice in this matter may be influenced by whether retail taxes routinely are included or are in addition to local asking prices.

Another point to consider when deciding if retail taxes should be included in the valuation amount is the "cashing out" option available to the insurance company when a claim is settled. The choice of whether a loss will be compensated for by replacement or a cash settlement is usually at the option of the insurer and if the cash settlement option is chosen it would not be appropriate for money which would otherwise have gone in payment of taxes to be paid to the insured because the insured is not Inland Revenue or the treasurer of a government or government department.

Finally, taxes levied on an article based upon its value, such as at the customs office when returning from abroad, consider the value of the article itself and not the value of the article plus the applicable taxes.

By excluding retail taxes from the opinion of value, or appending them to the opinion of value, and saying so on the appraisal document; or by declaring which taxes are included and their percentages, the appraiser makes the document user-friendlier. It is then easier for the document to serve useful functions beyond the original stated purpose. An example case might be a "voluntary declaration" situation where a young lady learns (from a jealous rival) that the diamond ring she received from her fiancée while on vacation should have been declared upon her return and appropriate taxes paid. To correct her innocent oversight, remove the stigma of "smuggled" from her symbol of pureness and love, and silence her rival she may voluntarily declare the importation of the ring to the customs authorities and offer to pay any taxes due based on the insurance valuation. In such a case it is better if the appraised value excludes the retail taxes.

Former tax structures may also be relevant. For example to establish the appropriate Canadian value prior to January 1st 1991 the former hidden federal manufacturer's tax (now replaced by the GST) must be considered.

Once all costs have been established a ***mark-up*** is applied to those costs to bring the amount up to retail. The mark-ups applied to cost (inclusive of hidden taxes) vary widely within the jewellery industry and depend upon a number of factors.

The first factor is costing point, which is where the retailer's wholesale cost lies within the range of lowest to highest wholesale. Large volume multi-location retailers achieve lower unit costs through bulk purchasing, which allows for larger mark-ups while still being competitive. Smaller volume single location retailers usually need to use lower mark-ups to remain competitive, although some such retailers may join with others to form buying groups and thus reduce their costing point.

The second factor that influences mark-up is the **type of goods**. The desirability of the merchandise is particularly significant. Articles that the public generally considers to be highly desirable tend to be able to bear a higher mark-up than those the public generally considers to be more mundane.

Machine made gold, jewellery of mediocre workmanship or condition, and production run jewellery having no gemstones of consequence may be given a basic mark-up. Cultured pearls, gemstone set jewellery, and superior quality plain metal jewellery may be given a somewhat higher standard mark-up. Diamond set jewellery and fine quality "designer type" jewellery with or without stones may warrant a fine jewellery mark-up, which is the highest mark-up.

The third factor influencing the mark-up is the **total cost**. A retailer may apply a higher mark-up to a lower cost article in stock but, if the same retailer has a client interested in a very expensive item that he can show from an approval memorandum (where he does not have to pay for the article until it is sold), he may be satisfied with a much lower mark-up. This suggests that mark-ups applied to cost should be on a sliding scale with lower cost items bearing a higher percentage mark-up and higher cost items having a lower percentage mark-up.

The fourth factor influencing the mark-up is the **retail price point.** A retailer usually tries to offer articles in a range of asking prices. He may reduce or increase a mark-up percentage to place the retail asking price within a particular price range.

By defining the hypothetical vendor as a single location small volume retailer who produces or acquires stock on a single item or minimum quantity basis, one sets perceived costs at high wholesale levels. Information about prices of goods, component materials, and workmanship at this wholesale level is readily available, but one must understand that the appropriate mark-ups to these costs will be lower than some retailers use because the mark-up is being applied to costs that are necessarily high.

When doing appraising the retail price point factor's influence on mark-up can be ignored. It would be unrealistic to specify the precise range and content of the inventory of our hypothetical vendor. The other three factors, however, must be considered. Our hypothetical single location vendor could not use the three or four times mark-up that some multi-location bulk buying retailers employ, yet fine jewellery will still bear a larger mark-up than standard or basic jewellery and higher cost items should have a lower percentage mark-up. (See p124 for example mark-up schedules.)

It is critical to understand that the costing approach can **only** be used in cases where one can ascertain the acquisition or production costs for the hypothetical vendor and where the hypothetical vendor would indeed be part of the most common market for like articles.

CAUTION Not all jewellery can be valued by the costing approach because this approach assumes that comparable new articles can be typically found in the hypothetical vendor's establishment. Examples of items for which the costing approach may not be appropriate can include:

o Rare or one-of-a-kind articles
o Memorabilia or collectibles
o Period jewellery
o Antiques
o Work by a named deceased designer/craftsman
o Religious artefacts
o Ethnic artefacts and native art objects
o Articles with organic material from endangered species
o Items with value related to history or prior ownership (provenance).

For items that are not readily replaceable with comparable new jewellery, the costing approach is less valid and the most common market may not be a jewellery store. For example, antique dealers or specialists would be more usual vendors of antique jewellery. An exceptional one-of-a-kind item by a renowned deceased craftsman might be more commonly sold at an auction.

Market data comparison

The most defensible approach for valuing any item is **market data comparison,** particularly at fair market value. This approach is the most time-consuming and expensive because it bases value on research into the actual marketplaces of comparable items to establish the cost of the article for the hypothetical purchaser. The article is considered as one complete article with particular qualitative and compositional properties, not as the sum of its parts.

Comparable items are of equivalent design, composition, quality, condition, rarity, origin, period, and (if it influences the value) by the same or comparable designer or craftsman.

Comparing numbers

In analysing the results of research it should be appreciated that there are different ways of comparing the data collected. Taking the average of all numbers uncovered by research may yield entirely inappropriate conclusions. Some data may be of greater significance than others. The following represents four different methods of comparing numbers.

If one adds all of the numbers together and divides the total by how many numbers there are, one will arrive at a simple average. This may be entirely inappropriate because it inherently assumes that every number considered is equally valid.

If one adds the highest number and the lowest number together and divides their total by two the result will be just as far from one extreme as the other but it entirely ignores intermediate samples which may be more important.

A statistically meaningful number called the median is that point below (and above) which 50% of the observations fall. To find the median eliminate the highest and lowest number, then repeat until only two or one number is left. If one number is left it is the median. If two numbers are left add them together and divide by two to get the median.

The most statistically significant number is called the mode. To find the mode one would examine the entire sampling and choose which number occurs most frequently.

Considering the following series of numbers: 330, 350, 350, 350, 350, 360, 370, 370, 380, 400, 430, 430, 460, 530; the simple average of all the numbers is 390, the number 430 is half way between the extremes, the median is 370 and the mode is 350.

The mode is the most appropriate to use when prudently considering a series of prices or costs.

Income approach

The third theoretical valuation approach is based on the ability of a property to generate income. It is only valid for income-producing property and is rarely applicable to jewellery. It is conceivable that someone might consider investing in jewellery to be rented or leased and in this case the income approach could be appropriate. It considers how much money the item will generate in a specified period of time rather than how much the item may have cost, would cost to replace, or how much one could get for it upon liquidation. Should a case arise when this method must be used, confer with an accountant for specifics.

Valuation approach overview

In the final analysis, market data comparison is crucial to the appraiser, but this is not to say the market data approach is the only valid way to appraise.

In the purest case, where identical items are readily available, data about buyer costs for that item in the most common market is clearly the most valid information upon which to base a valuation, with no consideration whatever given to the cost or value of component parts.

In cases where there are consequential differences between comparable articles in the marketplace, the degree to which the separate value of component parts have to be considered depends upon the degree by which the articles differ in their component parts. The greater the differences, the greater must be the consideration of the separate value of the components. The valuation approach thus shifts away from pure market data comparison toward a "costing approach" modified variation of it.

The importance of component materials can, however, be overshadowed by the provenance of an item which, contrary to the appearance of the word, has little to do with what can be proven, so long as the provenance is credible. The more significant the provenance, the less will be the influence of component values on the overall value of the article. For example, a silver and a gold locket each containing a lock of hair have components with significantly different values, but that difference in intrinsic value of the components (i.e. the gold and silver) may be entirely obscured by provenance. Documentation confirming a particular person as a previous owner of the locket could obscure the value related to its composition and, to an even greater extent, documentation confirming that the lock of hair inside the locket came from and was grown by a particular person could partially or completely obscure value considerations related to previous ownership (see **Provenance** p60)!

Within the costing approach, where the value of an article is established according to the sum of its parts, the costing of each component must be based upon valid data in an appropriate marketplace for those components. This means that market data comparison should be used to establish component costs as part of the costing approach to valuation. Furthermore, when comparable items readily available in the market place have only inconsequential differences between them, market data comparison of the article as a unit can confirm or refute the accuracy of the costing approach that has been set up to consider cases with more consequential differences.

In the end the appraiser must consider the article as a whole as well as consider its components to give a valid and defensible opinion of the article's place in the real world.

The final test of the value of any article is what it actually sells for when both the vendor and the purchaser have full knowledge of all relevant facts and neither is under any compulsion. All else is hypothesis, and this includes all appraisals whatever valuation approach is used. The appraiser should be able to explain the basis for that hypothesis and understand that validation of conclusions can only be established by market data comparisons, either as an approach in its own right or in pricing the components of the costing approach.

Insurance

It is worth looking at what insurance is and how it works before considering the various types of appraisals.

Tangible property, in general terms, is property other than real estate that has a physical existence and can be perceived by touch.

The owner of tangible property may recognise the possibility that possession or use of that property could be in jeopardy from a number of risks. When a loss would be particularly difficult to endure, the owner of such property may choose to apply some resources to ameliorate any possible future loss.

One approach to making a future loss more endurable is to set aside specific resources (such as put money into a special account) on a regular ongoing basis to accumulate a buffer to assist in weathering a loss. This approach can be very effective over the long term, but in the short term the accumulated dedicated resources may not be sufficient to balance out or even make a significant impression in a major loss.

Another approach is to apply some resources to have someone else undertake the risk. This is called insurance.

A fee is paid by the insured to the insurer under a contract that is drawn up based upon the principle of "utmost good faith"; the insurer trusting the insured to disclose all elements of risk under which coverage is sought and the insured trusting that the insurer will make good any loss suffered by the insured within the rules of the contract.

There are three broad types of insurance most often used to cover tangible property such as jewellery. These are:
- o   Standard replacement insurance,
- o   Guaranteed replacement insurance, and
- o   Value insurance.

With **standard replacement** insurance, the insurance company will repair or replace most covered jewellery items that are damaged or lost in order to leave the client in the same situation that existed before the loss occurred, or will indemnify the client for the difference between the value of the insured item before the loss and the value of the insured item after the loss up to the limit of coverage established by the value which served as the basis for calculating the insurance premiums.

If the cost of repair or replacement would exceed the value that served as the basis for calculating the insurance premiums, then the insurance company may pay the insured the value stated in the policy to satisfy their obligation under the insurance contract. Under standard replacement insurance, the insurer's liability is the lesser of the repair cost, the replacement cost, or the value that served as the basis for calculating the insurance premiums.

This is far and away the most usual type of insurance for jewellery under standard content insurance, comprehensive content insurance, or scheduled content insurance. This type of insurance is so prevalent that many insurance brokers or agents may believe it to be the only kind of insurance available for jewellery, and may even try to dissuade clients from seeking coverage on any other basis.

As much as is possible, agents, brokers and insurance companies in general want to write insurance of this standard type that is familiar and unexceptional. Anything unfamiliar or exceptional reduces the attractiveness of writing insurance from the point of view of the insurer. They make money on overall averages of typical cases! Special, unusual, or exceptional cases can't be judged on the basis of the historical averages of typical cases, which is how the expected profitability of most jewellery insurance is judged.

Guaranteed replacement insurance is a more expensive type of insurance where the insurer's liability is not limited by value. The insurer guarantees to provide full replacement in the event of a loss regardless of the cost.

Value insurance is the type of coverage that would be appropriate for an article that is irreplaceable from the point of view of a knowledgeable disinterested party who is at arms length. In such a case, insurance coverage should be for value rather than replacement. This can occur when all potential comparables have such significant or consequential differences that the only approach suitable for establishing the value of the item is to consider how much the article itself might realise if offered for sale on the open market (with duly defined or appropriately presumed vendor and purchaser).

In such cases the opinion of value by the expert becomes a declared value by the client when he submits the appraisal as the basis for insuring the item. This declared value becomes an agreed value when the insurance company accepts to underwrite the policy in the full knowledge that the item is not readily replaceable. The insurance coverage in such cases would be for value, not for replacement. When this point is understood, it is clear that the phrase "*not readily replaceable*" must not be casually used, and would be completely misused to describe any article accompanied by a valuation level named "...replacement...".

A loss suffered under value insurance is compensated by payment of money to the insured rather than by replacement, and it is very rare to have value insurance on a replaceable item.

In the insurance industry there are a number of different people who may be involved at some time or in some circumstances with an insured client. These include the broker (or agent), underwriter, adjuster, and investigator. Presuming that the investigator will not be called in because the appraiser and client are honest, upstanding people, we will take a brief look at the others.

An insurance **broker** provides the service of connecting clients to insurance that is best suited to their needs and market position. The broker advises each client as to the appropriate types of insurance and translates the content and wording of any contract. He ostensibly works for the client, but is paid on a commission basis by the insurance company. His freedom to offer alternatives will depend upon how many companies he represents. Thus, the larger his business the less likely he is to be under the control of any particular insurance company. His ability to offer personal service will also depend on the size of the company, with the tendency that the smaller company is somewhat more likely to recognise each client on a one-to-one basis rather than treating the client as an anonymous account. Thus the smaller his business the more likely the client is to get personal service.

An insurance **underwriter** works for the insurance company screening new policies to protect the insurance company from unacceptable risk. If the risk is too high, the underwriter will refuse the policy; if the risk is acceptable, or to the company's advantage, then the policy will be accepted.

The **adjuster** is the employee of the insurance company whose job it is to satisfy the claimant who has had a loss under the contract. Additionally, insurance companies expect an adjuster to keep the cost of claims down and also watch for fraudulent claims.

Most general home content insurance packages will cover jewellery up to a typical limit of $2,500 or $5,000 on jewellery and furs without the individual items being specified in the policy or even appraised. There is almost always a deductible written into the policy with the client covering the first $200 or $500 or other specified amount of any loss. Depending on the wording in the policy, the coverage may be for specified risks such as fire or burglary, or coverage may, with what is termed comprehensive coverage, be for all risks. All risk insurance would include such things as mysterious disappearance.

Listed (i.e. scheduled) articles are separately covered (in almost all cases on the basis of replacement) for all risks and there would usually be no deductible for a repair or replacement claim. The only contingencies that are normally not covered by "all risk" insurance are latent defects, wear and tear, gradual deterioration, war and/or revolution, or nuclear incident. Value insurance for listed articles is also possible but rare. The typical cost of listing jewellery articles is one to three percent per year of the article's value.

There is sometimes misunderstanding regarding who an in insurance appraisal has been produced for. One suggestion is that there is no point in considering who actually commissioned the appraisal because it may have been ordered and paid for by a number of different people. Regardless of whether the appraisal was commissioned by the designer, manufacturer, distributor, wholesaler, retailer, or consumer, this argument suggests that the end user of the appraisal will always be the insurance company when the insurance is written or when there is an insurance claim.

At first this sounds plausible, but it is completely wrong-ended; like the cart before the horse, or the tail wagging the dog. The end user is always the consumer. The appraisal may be used for other purposes, such as identifying jewellery taken on holiday abroad, and may never be used for insurance at all. When it is used for insurance it is the consumer who is seeking insurance on the appraised item(s) or seeking compensation for a loss under household contents insurance or some other blanket policy.

In the relationship between the consumer and the insurance company, it is always the consumer who provides all the information about what she wants to insure. If the consumer has an appraisal, she may offer that as information on which to base the insurance. If she has no documentation regarding what she wants to insure, the insurance company will suggest that she obtain an appraisal to submit with her request for coverage. It is never the insurance company that commissions the appraisal; it is always the consumer or someone who will provide the appraisal to the consumer "as a service".

The insurance company certainly has an interest in what the appraisal says, and the information of greatest interest to them will always be the appraised value because it immediately serves as the basis for calculating the insurance premiums to be paid. The two functions that value can perform for the insurance company is, be the basis for calculating premiums, and be the upper limit of their liability in the event of a loss. They want the consumer, their client, to be responsible for advising them of the value. They do not want to have any responsibility for setting the value on which the insurance premium is based because, if they accept the client's information of value, then the client has had input into deciding the premium to be charged.

Value for insurance

> **Value for insurance**: (noun) the amount of money that is to serve as the basis for insuring the jewellery.

All insurance companies will agree on what is required on an appraisal for this value to be acceptable to them as the basis for insurance coverage. It should be **the full amount that might realistically be paid for an identical or a comparable** (whichever is specifically required) **item sold**

in an appropriate market (as defined by the hypothetical purchaser and vendor) **for the personal use of the ultimate or final customer**.

In the preceding sentence the phrases in parenthesis are offered as additional explanation from the point of view of the valuer, not as points presumed to be incorporated in the insurer's perspective.

Whenever an appraisal is to be used for insurance purposes the valuation **must** satisfy this requirement, period; full stop. If the value on an appraisal submitted by a client and accepted by the insurance company as the basis for insurance does not satisfy this requirement, then the insurance coverage is in jeopardy because the insurance company may claim that all elements of risk were not properly disclosed to them by the client (or by the expert acting on behalf of the client).

Deliberate misrepresentation would clearly be grounds for any insurance company to deny a claim but, even without contending a deliberate intention to defraud, an insurance company might rescind an insurance policy because the failure to properly disclose all risk violates the principle of utmost good faith. The loss claimed by the client could be disallowed on the basis that improperly disclosed risk invalidates the insurance agreement, and no insurance ever existed. Any insurance premiums that were paid by the client or on the client's behalf were paid in error and will be partially (expenses deducted) or completely refunded by the insurance company.

In the event that a client suffers a loss and his insurance is rescinded because of an unrealistic valuation, liability of the appraiser for the client's loss may then be at issue because of the appraiser's obligations as a fiduciary (see fiduciary obligations, p140).

In choosing the valuation level for an insurance appraisal it is important to satisfy the standard insurance company requirement that the value presented by the client as the basis for insurance coverage be the full amount that would be paid for such an item for the personal use of the final consumer.

With our earlier definition of the purchaser and vendor, retail replacement value will certainly satisfy this requirement for the vast majority of cases.

By defining the purchaser as the insurance company and defining the vendor as an insurance replacement specialist, the appraiser can logically contend that the replacement/reproduction valuation level also satisfies this requirement.

A valuation for insurance at the wholesale level would not be appropriate for most cases because most transactions at this level are not for the personal use of the final consumer. An exception, when wholesale could be an appropriate valuation level for insurance, is if the final consumer, or the spouse of the final consumer, were someone in the jewellery industry with ready access to goods at true wholesale.

Every appraiser should understand that an unrealistic value places the insured client in jeopardy of having the insurance rescinded by the insurance company after there has been a loss.

From the point of view of the insurer, an unrealistically low value understates the actual risk because more valuable items are more attractive targets for thieves and robbers, and so are in greater danger of being stolen. At the other extreme, an unrealistically high value exposes the insurance company to higher risk from fraud, not only by the insured but also by fraud perpetrated without the knowledge of the insured by someone motivated by personal reasons to benefit the insured.

It should be noted that in such cases, when a loss leads the insurance company to investigate the cost of replacement and the adjuster finds that the replacement cost differs from the coverage by such an extent that the value that served as the basis of insurance coverage is considered unrealistic, the issue of the insurance company's ability to rescind the insurance and refuse replacement or compensation need not rest on the cause of the loss.

If the courts find that the value was unrealistic, the judgement may then go on to find that the insurance contract is invalid and the insurance company bears no liability to replace or otherwise compensate.

A suggestion that the claim of unrealistic value should be made earlier, before a loss is suffered, will not hold. The insurance company could have had no reason to question the value prior to a loss obliging them to consider the replacement cost.

It is not feasible to expect the insurance company to independently investigate replacement cost at the time insurance coverage is sought. The additional expense involved in such extra investigations would drive the price of insurance up to entirely unacceptable levels. The person seeking insurance coverage must bear the responsibility to provide realistic information about all the risks inherent in any item for which she is seeking coverage.

To be fair to the insurance companies it should also be pointed out that the calculation of premiums for jewellery coverage is made with the presumption that the cost of claims will be significantly less than the specified coverage in the vast majority of cases. If the valuation level on all appraisals for insurance were to suddenly more closely reflect actual replacement costs, insurance companies would have to increase the percentage of value used to calculate the premiums so as to maintain a reasonable profit level.

As long as retail replacement value is most often the basis for insurance appraisals, other valuation levels will remain exceptional cases that insurance underwriters must decide whether to accept or decline and, if accepted what level of premium should be charged.

Unless specified otherwise, "comparable replacement" for insurance purposes should be interpreted with reference to value, utility, quantity, composition, quality, and date of manufacture; but without particular concern for origin of materials, specifics of design, or identity of the vendor. For items of relatively modern manufacture the unmodified term **comparable** should be interpreted to mean comparable new. For period pieces and antiques, the unmodified term *comparable* should be interpreted to include in meaning "*of similar period*", and in such cases should also include the condition of the item as a component of comparability.

All replacement requirements other than replacement with comparable, such as precise duplication in material and design, or replacement by the original designer/manufacturer, must be specifically stated.

The valuation level for insurance must be specified and, if necessary, defined to leave no doubt as to the category of vendor and purchaser appropriate to that level of valuation.

In scheduled pair-and-set insurance coverage the insurance company's liability for partial loss is usually limited to **the difference** between the value before a partial loss and the value afterward. That is to say the insurer, in settlement of a claim, will pay the insured the difference between what the set is now worth and what it was worth before the loss. If a set consisting of a pair of cufflinks with seven matching shirt studs is reduced to a set of cufflinks and six matching shirt studs, then the insured claiming a loss would be paid the difference in value between a set with seven studs and a set with six studs, **not** be given another set with seven shirt studs. The alternative is for the insured to purchase a broad pair-and-set endorsement (at an additional cost of about 1/2% per year of the value) wherein the insurer will either replace the lost part, or replace the full set in exchange for the remainder of the set when the insured suffers a partial loss.

Types of appraisals[7]

The name given to each type of appraisal indicates, where possible, the assigned use (p9) that should be specified within the appraisal document.

For insurance

An appraisal for insurance has a comprehensive description supporting an estimate of value. This type of appraisal:
- Identifies the item(s) to be insured
- Establishes a basis upon which insurance premiums are charged
- May provide the limit of the insurance company's liability in the event of a loss and
- Will be the basis of settlement of any claim if there is a loss.

---

[7] NOTE: This information is not legal opinion or legal advice. Reading, viewing, or receiving it does not create or constitute an attorney-client relationship. To the best of the author's knowledge and belief references herein to legislation, tax rules, administrative practices, and/or jurisprudence were up to date and correct at the time of writing, but laws, rules, practices, and legal rulings are continuously evolving. It is recommended that for cases having tax consequences, or of particular legal consequence, you consult with an accountant or lawyer of appropriate specialization for up to date information and advice. It is further suggested that you make a point of offering this same recommendation to any client you advise.

The appraiser may not know details of the insurance contract and should provide a comprehensive report suitable for whatever type of insurance may obtain. As the basis of settlement of a future repair or replacement claim, the accuracy and completeness of the description is of paramount importance.

Most appraisals for insurance assume that the vendor of a replacement article will be a quality jewellery retailer in the business of retailing like articles and not offering a discount. Any variance from this, with explanations where necessary, should be clearly specified on the appraisal. For coverage that is not value insurance, other valuation levels may be more appropriate (see valuation levels p10). An appraiser could consider using replacement/reproduction value for the client who wants adequate coverage and will accept replacement by a replacement-specialist who may not be a typical jewellery retailer. Duplication value may be more appropriate for a difficult to replace article requiring specialized custom work.

The valuation level for insurance must be specified and, if necessary, defined to leave no doubt as to the categories of the vendor and the purchaser that are appropriate to the level of valuation. It is important to understand that the value, which is to serve as the basis for insuring the jewellery, should be what might realistically be paid for an identical or a comparable item sold in an appropriate market for the personal use of the ultimate or final customer.

The insurance company will repair or replace most covered jewellery items that are damaged or lost in order to leave the client in the same situation that existed before the loss occurred, or will indemnify the client for the difference between the value of the insured item before the loss and the value of the insured item after the loss. Any replacement requirement other than replacement with comparable, such as precise duplication in material and design, or replacement by the original designer/manufacturer, must always be clearly specified.

Hypothetical for insurance

A hypothetical appraisal for insurance is a report of the expected cost of replacing an article that the appraiser has not seen and will not be able to examine. Usually it is for articles covered (or partially covered) by general content insurance that have been lost or stolen without having been appraised prior to the claim. It is an appraisal with extreme limiting conditions. Many major assumptions will have to be made based upon whatever evidence can be gleaned from interviews, photographs, old receipts, outdated appraisals or whatever the client can offer.

In this case replacement/reproduction value would be the most appropriate valuation level and the appraisal may be accompanied by an offer to replace. Alternatively, the appraisal may merely be documentation considered by the insurance company as "proof of loss" to serve as the basis for a cash settlement of the claim in the event that the insurance coverage is not sufficient to cover the cost of replacement in excess of the deductible.

In theory an offer to replace is not an appraisal, but in the same way that an insurance company can use a hypothetical appraisal as a proof of loss to cash out a claim, they will often accept a simple offer to replace as a proof of loss document. Because an offer to replace may be used this way, it is not unreasonable to charge a fee for a written offer to replace (similar to the fee for a hypothetical appraisal) and have that fee creditable toward the asking price of the replacement.

Probate

A probate appraisal is the type used by the legal community in the settling of an estate and, in almost all cases, will have a lower level of valuation (than an appraisal for insurance) that will depend on the jurisdiction.

In jurisdictions with no death duties or inheritance taxes the most appropriate valuation level would be liquidation value, which allows the executor to balance the value of the jewellery against cash in the bank when dividing the estate among beneficiaries.

In jurisdictions where government departments of revenue deem that, for purposes of calculating the deceased person's final income tax payment, all property was liquidated on the last full day of life, liquidation value would likely be most appropriate for calculating capital gain, although forced sale value could arguably be offered in some jurisdictions.

Other jurisdictions, particularly those with death duties or inheritance taxes (such as Quebec or most parts of the USA), may have very strict requirements regarding the valuation level for probate with heavy penalties to both the producer and user of the appraisal if valuation is at less than "fair market value". A probate appraisal should be clearly marked "FOR PROBATE ONLY" and "WHAT A WILLING PURCHASER WOULD PAY A WILL-ING VENDOR" with the optional addition to that last phrase of "IN A PROMPT DISPOSAL" or "ON LIQUIDATION" or "AT FAIR MARKET VALUE" as appropriate.

Property settlement

A property settlement appraisal is used when jointly owned assets must be divided between partners on dissolution of a relationship. This may be a marriage, business partnership or any other legal relationship with joint property. The valuation basis may be one of several and should coincide with the valuations used on the rest of the jointly owned property. Requirements may vary according to the jurisdiction, being usually either fair market value or liquidation value. In Ontario, for example, the method of calculating assets on dissolution of a marriage may be based on a notional sale of the assets less any disposition costs and less any taxes payable, which would be the liquidation value.

Donation

A donation appraisal applies to items donated to charitable organisations or to governments. It will be the basis on which tax relief will be granted to the donor. The usual valuation basis for a donation appraisal (required in most jurisdictions) is fair market value.

In Canada there are three main types of donations:
- o Charitable gifts to a registered charity (one able to provide an official receipt for income tax purposes) which may be applied to reduce tax payable with the amount of the value of the gift considered in calculating the tax credit being limited to a percentage of income for each eligible year (In Canada, 20% prior to 1996, 50% for 1996 and subsequent years; and 100% for bequests or legacies from 1996; unused claims may be carried

forward for up to five years, and may be carried back one year for gifts made in the year of death)

o   Crown gifts (to Her Majesty in right of Canada or a province), the value of which may be applied to reduce taxes payable and is not subject to the percentage of income limitation

o   Cultural gifts (after 1987) to an institution or public authority designated by the Cultural Property Export and Import Act (CPEIA) of an object which meets criteria in the Act and which has been certified by the Canadian Cultural Property Export Review Board, (CCPERB) whereupon the value of such a gift may be applied to reduce taxes payable and is not subject to the percentage of income limitation. (To get a copy of the Canadian Cultural Property Export Review Board's publication called *Applications for Certification of Cultural Property for Income Tax Purposes — Information and Procedures*, call the Review Board Secretariat at (613) 990-4161 or fax them at (613) 954-8826.)

THERE ARE CIRCUMSTANCES WHEN A DONATION IS **NOT** A GIFT.

Charitable deduction does not apply to a donation of property where its cost has been or should be charged as a business expense. For example, if someone transfers merchandise or supplies to a charity in consideration of a right, privilege, material benefit or advantage such as promotion or advertising then the transfer cannot be considered a gift and therefore is not deductible

Donors should also be aware of the income tax rule that, generally, when anything is disposed of by way of a gift the donor is deemed to have received proceeds equal to the fair market value of that gift and must therefore account for:

o   Income (under section 9 of the Act in Canada) if the property was inventory of a business, or

o   Capital gain or loss (under section 39 of the Act in Canada) if the property was a capital property, and

o   Recapture of capital cost allowance (under section 13 of the Act in Canada) if the property was depreciable property.

For Canadian donations claimed for the 1996 and subsequent taxation years, the normal 50% limit is raised to 100% on the portion of a donation of appreciated property that must be included in the donor's taxable income.

Government revenue departments try to limit tax loopholes and maximize tax revenue within the rules governed by legislation. Rules on valuation levels for articles donated to charities or to governments have varied significantly from time to time.

Current information circulars and interpretation bulletins about particular rules, charities, various kinds of gifts, deductible gifts and official donation receipts may be obtained from the tax services office or tax centre.

When the rules required that the actual cost (or the adjusted cost base) of the donated article would be the allowed basis for tax deduction, charitable organisations found that significantly fewer items were donated. It naturally followed that charitable organisations then strongly lobbied for relaxation of the rules.

In Canada current rules allow full capital gains exemption for Crown gifts and Cultural gifts (with the fair market value exceeding the cost of a donated article) tempered by administrative one, two, or three year holding period requirements that are not legislatively mandated. On each article of property donated to a charitable organisation the Canadian rules allow an adjusted cost base at an unsubstantiated $1,000 above actual cost which, when there are no substantiated allowable additional costs and, although it is an entirely different concept, has exactly the same effect as would a capital gains exemption of up to $1,000 per article.

When an unset gemstone is donated, to a charity for example, the donor may be an individual rather than a business in the jewellery industry. Fair market value on a loose gemstone would normally assume a transaction within the industry rather than at retail because that is the most common marketplace for unset stones. To specify **retail fair market value** could be appropriate under the more relaxed rules when the donor is an individual. If the charity's tax receipt shows a value up to $1,000 more than the donor's cost, the full amount of the value of the gift can be claimed without requirement to declare any capital gain because of the allowable adjusted cost base. In valuing an unset stone for a donation appraisal, one may choose to hypothesise the stone as being in a setting to rationalize a retail value. One might even go so far as to have the report read in part "...If this gemstone were mounted in an item of fine jewellery the portion of the fair market value attributable to this stone would be…" although it would be equally valid to just specify "retail fair market value" while following this rationalization. Bear in mind, however, that it is not appropriate to use retail replacement value (p17) for donation appraisals. This is to say in more simplistic terms, for "retail fair market value" consider typical retail, not highest retail!

The appraiser of a donated article should be "at arms length" from the principals, that is to say should be entirely independent of the prospective donor as well as independent of the vendor to the prospective donor. He must have no vested interest in the sale or value of the article. Some charitable organisations will not accept appraisals that were commissioned by the vendor or prospective donor but will instead commission the appraisal work themselves with names of the vendor and/or donor withheld from the appraiser.

Collateral

A collateral appraisal applies to items offered as security and a guarantee of payment or repayment of a debt, usually monetary. The valuation basis for this type of appraisal is usually liquidation value, forced sale value or, rarely, fair market value. The valuation level used should be understood and agreed upon by both the debtor and the debt holder. Although either the borrower or the lender may commission the collateral appraisal, the appraiser should consider himself responsible to both parties. The wording and explanation in the report should clearly define and explain the valuation level(s) used.

Resale

An appraisal for resale would apply to jewellery offered for sale in the secondary marketplace including private sales, estate departments, used goods dealers, and liquidation sales. Fair market value would be the most appropriate valuation level, although liquidation value could be considered in some cases. Duplication value, retail replacement value, or replacement/reproduction value would be entirely inappropriate in an appraisal for resale. The stated purpose has nothing to do with reproducing, replacing with new, or duplicating the item.

Market comparison

Prospective jewellery purchasers who do not have the time, ability or inclination to comparison shop could commission a market comparison appraisal. Fair market value would be the most appropriate valuation level, although a range of values might also be reported. Duplication value, retail replacement value, or replacement/reproduction value would be entirely inappropriate in a market comparison appraisal because the stated purpose has nothing to do with reproducing, replacing with new, or duplicating any item.

Special appraisals

Special appraisals are also possible but relatively rare. For example one might be commissioned by a government or police department to inspect and report on articles of consequence in a tax decision or criminal investigation. In such cases a more formal and detailed format is usually required (see p129), often including as part of the report an Appraiser's Certificate indicating the extent of the appraiser's interest (if any) in the article(s) examined. The valuation level is usually fair market value although other valuation levels may be specified.

Another special appraisal that may be encountered is an appraisal report to auditors for goods owned by a company with an absent silent partner. The documentation format and content as well as the valuation level(s) would be established according to the auditors' wishes which, depending on the marketing level of the company, may be any of the aforementioned (except perhaps retail replacement value or duplication value) or may be a special level of valuation of particular relevance to the individual case.

Appraising procedures

Having due consideration for the theory already covered, it is necessary to face the practicalities of performing a valuation. This means looking at the process in general terms as well as considering the procedural details.

The process ... take-in to pickup

Take-in

When the property is received it must be accompanied by information as to requirements for the appraisal. What information does or will the client require, in what circumstances, and for what purposes?

<u>Whose appraisal?</u> It should be addressed to someone!

First the holder of the property, the person or entity who is commissioning the appraisal, **must** be identified. In most cases this will be the purported owner and as the goods are being received at the take-in counter the name, address and telephone number(s) should be recorded.

In some cases the name and address of the owner may be omitted from the instructions to the appraiser, in which case the appraiser should automatically put the name of the retailer on the appraisal, such as "client of ABC Jewellery" with perhaps a reference number, leaving room on the document for the retailer to insert the customer's name. It is also appropriate to identify the client by file name or file number and the name of the company, institution or government department requiring the appraisal. Some clients, for reasons of personal security, may require that their address and telephone number not be placed on the appraisal, in which case the take-in clerk should indicate which information is confidential and is not to be put on the final document.

It is not appropriate for an appraisal to open with "To whom it may concern" or be addressed to no one at all. An appraisal should properly be addressed to a specific individual or organisation. The appraisal is, after all, an official record of an expert's report to someone.

Most appraisal work is on valuable items, so confidentiality is usually an important consideration. "To whom it may concern" or no address at all implies that the communication is an open or public document, which is not often appropriate. Occasionally an appraiser may be asked questions regarding documents, and if each appraisal is addressed to a specific person or institution it is clearer who is entitled to information and confidentiality can be better maintained.

Inventory of items.

As the goods are being taken in they should be catalogued. Each item in the catalogue of inventory may be a single article, a pair of articles, or a set of a specified number of articles according to how they are to be considered in the appraisal. At the conclusion of the list, the number of items (not the number of articles) should be specified. For example, the inventory of a ring, a watch, a pair of cuff links, and a set of five shirt studs would show a total of four items (not nine articles) and the description of each item would specify the details of the count.

Professional expertise should be reflected in the information set down in this catalogue of inventory. Examine each article carefully for clues of identification. Qualify any tentative identification with the word "apparent", and simply describe items that cannot be identified. If the client offers identification of an article, which, upon examination seems doubtful but cannot at that point be disputed, use wording such as "purported" or "claimed" or place the questionable identification within quotation marks. Make it clear to the client that identifications at take-in are tentative and are subject to confirmation or reversal by laboratory analysis.

An alternative to doing preliminary identification work is to have the client list the items in his own words on part of the take in form (or the take-in clerk could record what the client dictates).

Thermal inertia testers are relatively inexpensive and provide instant rapid testing for high thermal conductivity coupled with electrical insulation. This used to allow easy identification of diamond or diamond topped assemblies. Now a less experienced employee taking in jewellery should be carefully instructed regarding visual identification of synthetic moisanite by observing double images of crown facet edges reflected in the pavilion, or of double images of the culet when viewed through crown main facets.

Make sure to identify without qualification only when there are reasonable grounds to do so. For example an article made of an alloy with less than nine parts gold in twenty-four cannot be called "gold" and is considered base metal in many parts of the world. However, not all jurisdictions have that nine-karat minimum standard. Vacationers in some places may be offered jewellery with eight twenty-fourths gold content that has been carefully marked "8K" with an apparently accidentally occurring vertical line in front of the eight. This is easy to misread as eighteen karat. If they bring such a ring in for appraisal it is more prudent to just describe the markings, perhaps by hand copying the apparent markings within quotation marks on the take-in form.

The take-in form should have a pre-printed notice that:
- o   The store does not warrant the client's identification of the article(s)
- o   Any identification(s) by the person taking in the article(s) are tentative because of the necessarily cursory nature of the examination
- o   All identifications are subject to confirmation or reversal by laboratory analysis and
- o   Liability in the event of any damage or loss caused by negligence is limited to the cost for replacement or repair and specifically excludes consequential damages and sentimental value.

The signature on the catalogue of inventory should be the **client's** not that of the take-in clerk. The client's signature confirms that the take-in form, including the inventory as well as the notice, was read and agreed to. The presence of his signature should serve to assure the client that the list on the form is indeed the original list when the goods are finally collected. For security purposes the store would keep all copies with the inventory and client's signature and give the client a receipt signed by the take-in clerk and numbered to coincide with the number on the take-in form. This receipt should **not** show the client's name or the catalogue of inventory, but may specify the number of items left for valuation.

A receipt which lists the items and the client's name is placing the client in significant unnecessary jeopardy because an unscrupulous person who steals or otherwise acquires the receipt may then, upon simply paying the appraisal fee while claiming to be the owner, steal the jewellery. A more subtle and dangerous scenario wherein the client is jeopardised is having someone simply see the receipt and at a glance learning information about the client's tangible property which should remain confidential and which could set the client up as a potential target for robbery or burglary.

Condition of goods

At take-in is the appropriate time to carefully examine the jewellery with regard to condition, pointing out to the customer if any repair work is advisable or if anything is damaged. This will eliminate any possibility of the customer trying to hold the jeweller responsible for the costs of re-tipping and re-setting stones that fall out of worn settings during cleaning, or replacing stones that may have been unknowingly damaged by the owner. It is also an opportunity to get authorization to arrange for necessary *repairs* **to the jewellery** *before* **the appraisal is finalised**, so the appraisal will be based on the final condition of the jewellery and not have to describe damaged or worn items unsafe to wear because of needed repairs.

There is one point that should be clearly understood by the jewellery owner and anyone who holds someone else's goods: when accepting custody of someone else's property there is an obligation to care for that property at least as carefully as a reasonable person would in the same situation. The level of care with which other goods are handled may be almost irrelevant. Everyone is entitled to handle his own goods negligently (and suffer any results). The central point in any dispute is

what would be reasonable for the hypothetical average person in a like situation. Law of bailment requires that one must show the reasonable care assessed by the standard set by the prudent man. If negligence causes damage, there is a liability for whatever wrong that negligence has caused subject to the limits of liability that were agreed upon by the client at take-in.

An additional point of significance is that regardless of responsibility for the handling of someone's property, temporary custody does ***not*** in any way imply responsibility for ***the condition*** of the property. As an example, consider that while examining an item for appraisal a stone falls out. There is no liability for the costs of remounting the stone into the article because the cause of it coming loose was the condition of the article, not negligence. The appropriate thing to do in this case is to advise the client and seek authorization to have the necessary repairs done before issuing the final appraisal. To extend the case, if the stone that fell out was then swallowed by a pet crow that flew off into the wild blue yonder, there would be a responsibility to replace the stone, but not to repair the article and mount the replacement.

A corollary to this principle is that work done on any article is always at the risk of the owner of the article, not at the risk of the conscientious worker or any intermediary. Wilful action or negligence (by commission or omission) can be grounds for liability but accident or misadventure is not. It sometimes happens that a damaged stone is replaced without extra charge to the consumer. Only where the damage was due to negligence is replacement without charge obligatory. In cases where there was no negligence, free replacement is not required but is, rather, a goodwill gesture that makes sense if the stone is inexpensive. If work has to be done on jewellery set with valuable stones it would be wise to ensure that the client understands that work must always be at the owner's risk.

Another point to bear in mind is that it is always helpful to know the actual weight of a stone in an item being appraised. If a stone has fallen out of a setting or if a new stone is being supplied to replace a lost or damaged stone, the appraiser should not miss the opportunity to measure, weigh, and grade the loose stone!

Purpose & valuation level

What is the purpose of the appraisal? Most appraisals are for insurance but this is not always the case. Many people do not know that there can be different kinds of appraisals at wide ranging valuation levels and will ask for an "appraisal for insurance" when they intend to use it for an entirely different purpose. Have a bit of a chat with them and ask a few questions that will confirm how they intend to use the appraisal.

If the appraisal is to be used in settlement of property rights in a divorce, for example, establish whether fair market value, liquidation value, or forced sale value is required (see p10 to p19 for definitions of various valuation levels).

To fulfil third party obligations make sure that the valuation level is understood and agreed upon by both parties if doing a collateral appraisal or, failing that, be sure that the contents of the appraisal cannot be accidentally or deliberately misrepresented by one party to the other. It would be appropriate to quote and define the value at two or three appropriate valuation levels if one party commissions a collateral appraisal while refusing to consider the appraiser's obligations to other people.

Sometimes someone will want to sell an article and will seek an appraisal saying they "just want to know what it's worth". Avoid this sort of guessing game by refusing to play. Discuss it with the client to ascertain **why** they want to know what it is worth and, if necessary, explain valuation levels to them.

Valuation date

What should be the valuation date of the appraisal? It may not necessarily be the date on which the appraisal work is performed. For example, if the purpose of the appraisal is to establish the value in the case of a divorce proceeding, a more appropriate valuation date could be the date the spouses separated. To probate a Last Will and Testament the Trustee of the estate may specify the last full day of life of the deceased or some other date significant in valuing other property in the estate.

When the valuation date differs from the date the appraisal is performed this should be noted in boldface on the same line of the document containing the value or in equal prominence immediately adjacent to the value. The wording should indicate both the date and valuation basis, such as "LIQUIDATION VALUE in JUNE 1996" or "PROBATE VALUE AT DECEMBER 24th 1995". In the example for probate, the precise valuation level (e.g. fair market value or liquidation value) does not need to be specified if the jurisdiction clearly requires fair market value for probate.

Special requirements

At times there may be special requirements such as value based on replacement of the item with a reproduction by the original designer/manufacturer instead of replacement with a comparable item produced by an unspecified designer/manufacturer. If an item is not readily replaceable it must be determined whether the client would accept as compensation for loss a generally similar article of equal or greater worth, or does the client require that any replacement be as near identical to the original article as possible.

Special instructions

The take in clerk should always note any particular desires of the customer such as if the customer prefers one nomenclature to another, for example "Scan. D. N. grading please", or has concerns about an item, such as "please take care to preserve the patina on this silver brooch, do not polish or clean."

Declaration of value

It may, at first blush, seem inappropriate to ask for a declaration of value from someone seeking an appraisal. It must be clearly understood by all parties that the declared values are completely unrelated to the appraised values and are merely to provide the owner with adequate coverage while the property is in the store's custody.

One approach is to suggest to the client that access to goods at true wholesale prices could allow an outdated retail replacement value to serve as a declared value that would provide adequate insurance coverage while the jewellery is in the store's custody. It would not be entirely inappropriate for the take in clerk to suggest a declared value if the client draws a complete blank. Clearly, however, it avoids confusing the declared value with an appraised value if the client independently makes the declaration. If a client insists upon an unrealistically high declared value, it would be best to simply decline to accept custody of the item on the basis of such an unacceptable risk.

If the property is stolen, destroyed, lost or damaged without a prior declaration of value it may be extremely difficult to mutually agree on a settlement after the fact. The difficulty of eliciting a declaration of value will be much less than the problems inherent in settling a claim without one, which might require third party arbitration, perhaps even litigation. (See the section entitled Liability and Responsibility starting on p138.)

Performing the appraisal

In typical cases the costing approach may be used to arrive at an estimate of value. Within this approach one must establish all of the costs to the hypothetical vendor for producing the article and decide on an appropriate mark-up (or deduction) for the required valuation level.

Procedures

The steps involved are:
- 1. Preliminary examination.
- 2. Inspect and clean.
- 3. Begin description.
- 4. Assay (if necessary), weigh and measure.
- 5. Identify stones
- 6. Count and measure stones
- 7. Estimate the weight of stones
- 8. Quality grade stones
- 9. Calculate the perceived cost of stones
- 10. Calculate raw metal value

- 11. Analyse design and construction labour cost
- 12. Calculate setting cost
- 13. Add the raw metal value and all costs together
- 14. Factor in hidden taxes (if applicable)
- 15. Add a mark-up (or subtract as necessary) to reach the required valuation level
- 16. Round off to an appropriate number of digits
- 17. Consider if the conclusion of value is reasonable, reconsider and revise as necessary, noting rationale for changes
- 18. Complete the description and type the appraisal
- 19. Reread the typed appraisal carefully before signing it
- 20. Sign, seal and package the appraisal
- 21. Produce an invoice
- 22. Arrange for pickup or delivery.

Preliminary examination

If someone else performed the take-in, the appraiser will need to **personally** examine each article and make the preliminary decision as to whether go any further.

- Is it appropriate to appraise the item?

If it is costume[8] jewellery, base metal, or an otherwise inexpensive item, the customer may be better served (and appreciate the savings) if the item is merely identified rather than fully appraised.

- What is the condition of the item?

If repairs are needed to make the item serviceable, or if repairs are advisable, get instructions from the owner about how to proceed. Do they want the item repaired before it is appraised? Do they want the item appraised as it is and the appraisal updated after the repair work is done? Do they want the item appraised as it is without being repaired, and if so why?

---

[8] Costume: (noun) full set of outer garments worn for a particular activity, attire and hairstyle of a specific ethnic group and/or period, apparel and accessories for which superficial appearance is the paramount criterion of suitability; **(adjective) having superficial appearance as the prime criterion of desirability**.

o   Is it an article requiring **special expertise?**

An appraiser not competent to appraise the article should refer the client to someone who is, or subcontract that portion of the appraisal work.

Having decided to proceed with the appraising, make initial notes to incorporate into the description and make a preliminary diagnosis of the possible identities of the gemstones to help decide the method of cleaning to be used.

Cleaning jewellery

Ultrasonic cleaners are particularly good at loosening tenacious grime, and steam cleaners do an admirable job of blasting away loosened human detritus to leave surfaces sparkling clean. They do their jobs well because of their vigorous action, which can permanently damage some stones.

Choose the method of cleaning according to the preliminary diagnosis of the possible identities of the gemstones mounted in the article and try to always err on the side of caution.

I have seen a small pile of emerald gravel that I was told was the remains of the centre stone from a ring put in an ultrasonic cleaner. I have also seen a very fine quality opal triplet that had been partially de-laminated after prolonged exposure to the heat of a steam cleaner. Such action would indeed be negligence because any jewellery professional should know better!

Whatever cleaning method is used, be sure to take precautions to catch gems that come out of their settings during cleaning. With some items that will be encountered, the only thing holding a stone in position may be the dirt surrounding it. If the layers of dirt are thick enough the condition may not have been discernible in the preliminary examination. The same rule applies here for discovery of needed repairs; get instruction from the owner about how to proceed.

Describing jewellery

The writing of jewellery descriptions is somewhat of an art, however, it is good to remind oneself of the purposes and applications of appraisal documents, few of which would hinge upon artistic merit. Literary style and arresting rhetoric may have their place but that is not in appraisals, where it is much more important to record information clearly and concisely with the minimum potential for misinterpretation.

A superior appraisal will more than satisfy the stated requirements of the client and will do so in a package the client can read with ease and comfort and will find understandable. To achieve this the jewellery description in an appraisal should contain

- All necessary components,
- Full detail,
- As little extraneous verbiage as possible,
- The document should be formatted to
- Facilitate easy access to the information,
- Be easy to read and understand, and
- Appear attractive and professional.

A point format report may be adequate as to content but is not easy or comfortable for most clients to read. It is most likely to be perceived as an accumulation of stilted and disconnected bits of data requiring mental gymnastics to see the overall picture. It tends to leave the impression that the appraiser was either unwilling or unable to integrate the data into a finished whole.

Clients are much more likely to be comfortable reading a report written in a narrative format. In the narrative format information is presented in a conversational manner easy for the client to read and follow, and this style of appraisal leaves the client feeling that the document is a coherent unit.

The art lies in crafting the words so they flow together smoothly in sentences that logically follow one another. The following are a few points to bear in mind as descriptions are developed.

- Think of the description as a précis of the appraiser's conclusions.
- Keep all descriptions as concise as possible.
- Avoid repetition of words or phrases.
- Develop a vocabulary of standard jewellery terminology.
- Establish a standardized sequence of information for like articles and for like jewellery components.
- String adjectives and modifiers together in standard sequences avoiding ambiguities.
- Proceed from the general to the specific.
- Use proper punctuation to maintain the sense and flow.

The components of a **proper description** should include: type of item, design, composition, qualities, quantification, condition, authenticity, and provenance when it is significant.

Type of item
Name the general category of item such as ring, bracelet, necklace, earrings, diadem, brooch, pendant, pocket watch, chatelaine, cuff links, etc.

Design
Describe the appearance of the item including the configuration, size, shape, proportions, and perhaps naming a recognized style, period, or place that indicates design style, such as "Bohemian garnet necklace". If an article is in the design of a particular meaningful character or symbol and/or bears an inscription in a foreign language it would be quite appropriate to have the client provide a translation to incorporate into the report and indicate that it was "translated by the client".

Composition
Specify the identity of all component materials, kinds of metals, composition of non-gem materials, species and varieties of all stones and extent to which they are artificially enhanced or treated, if it can be determined. As an example a sapphire which careful examination shows is not synthetic and has not undergone diffusion treatment or cavity filling and which has no clear indication of heat treatment may simply be called

"sapphire", whereas a sapphire with melted inclusions and halo stress fractures should be identified as heat treated.

Know the requirements of the intended jurisdiction for the appraisal. In Great Britain, for example, it is an infraction of the hallmarking law to describe as gold, silver, or platinum any article that does not bear a hallmark unless the article is of minimum fineness and meets the requirements for exemption.

Qualities
Report the attractiveness and marketability of design (i.e. its general appeal rather than personal appeal), execution of design, workmanship, quality of metals, colour/clarity/make of gemstones, qualities of each phenomenon in phenomenal coloured stones, and appropriate quality descriptions of all component materials.

Quantification
Show enumerations and weights. This is the number of and type of articles included in a set and the number, sizes, and weights of stones in them. It includes the gross weight of the item or set of like items, or average gross weight of each like item in a set.

Condition
Consider whether the item is new, slightly worn, worn, very worn, dangerously worn, or damaged. For some appraisals, it is appropriate to choose **not to report ordinary wear** common to the type of article when the extent of wear is slight, worn, or very worn. For example normal wear would not be relevant in an insurance appraisal at retail replacement value or at reproduction replacement value on an article that would as a matter of course be replaced with new jewellery.

Under the principal of "utmost good faith" central to all insurance contracts, dangerously worn or damaged condition should be reported as a matter of course in an appraisal for insurance. That is because such condition is very significant in establishing the insurability of the item and/or the risk that the insurance company will undertake for the premium to be paid.

If examination for an insurance appraisal update discloses that prongs holding a stone are dangerously worn, for example, then it is incumbent on the owner to have the necessary repairs done. The repairs are needed to safeguard the stone as well as keep up the insurance coverage. If the owner declines to have the work done and the stone is then lost, the insurer could disallow a claim of loss because of inadequate maintenance.

Provenance

Dealers in antiques, period pieces, and collectibles understand that provenance can have a considerable influence on value. This issue can also be extremely important for jewellery. It is every bit as significant for brand new items as it is for older pieces. Curiously, provenance as a concept has little or nothing to do with whether or not something can be proven. In theory, provenance has more to do with province than proof!

Provenance, in its purest sense, means the origin of the item, particularly the place of origin (from whence it came). The concept has grown beyond geography to include the items history, particularly related to (famous or infamous) people who have had contact with it. It has been considered to be almost a property of the item and an antique dealer may ask if an item has provenance, which is assumed to mean "Does this item have a significant provenance and if so what is it and is there supporting documentation?" It would be a grammatical error to speak of an article as having no provenance because everything must have originated somewhere sometime.

A non-jewellery example of a statement of provenance in this broad sense of historical connection could be a sign attached to an antique bed saying, "George Washington slept here." This is clearly a statement of provenance whether or not there is supporting proof or documentation. The plausibility of the stated provenance will depend upon the evidence.

Famous or infamous person(s) may be individuals, companies, or definable groups; and the contact of the person with the item may be in its design, manufacture, sale, outright ownership of, or even simple proximity.

The significance of the provenance in each case depends upon the time and place of origin and the importance of the person(s) historically connected to the item as well as the weight of evidence supporting the provenance.

A statement of provenance would normally not be considered plausible without supporting evidence. Credible evidence of an item's provenance may be in composition and design, packaging, trademarks, a signature on the item, or an accompanying document such as a bill of sale, warranty, photograph, customs document, a sworn affidavit, a written expert opinion, a last will and testament, a note referencing a will, a letter mentioning the item, clippings from printed material about the item, or even unrelated but clearly dated or traceable material such as newspaper used for packing. Mention of references in publicly available literature, even oral traditions or a personal verbal communication may also be credible evidence of provenance in some circumstances. Credulity, rather than technical analysis, is what is more often tested by evidence of provenance.

Branding, a central issue in much modern marketing, has everything to do with provenance. The vendor of every brand seeks to establish a cachet of increased value specific to the brand.

Branding of an item does not automatically give it any significant provenance, however. The value relationship of provenance has nothing at all to do with whether or not an item is branded. It has everything to do with the reputation of the person(s) attributed to in the provenance. Branding provides evidence of provenance, and nothing more. A relatively new item trademarked by an unknown manufacturer has insignificant provenance and an insurance replacement by an anonymous supplier that satisfied the item's description in all other particulars would be perfectly appropriate.

An anonymous supplier would not be appropriate to replace a solitaire diamond ring with the distinctive Asprey setting and their trademark, for example. Provenance would require replacement by Asprey's (or by one of the very few houses of comparable repute).

Utility
Suitability or usefulness in the marketplace can influence the desirability of an item.

Although utility may not be a matter the appraiser will want to directly address as part of the description, the details of the description should be sufficient and complete enough for the knowledgeable dealer or savvy buyer to recognise the level of utility from the description. Such things as style, size, design, and type of item are things that can influence utility as much or more than condition in some cases.

Because utility can very significantly influence the saleability of an item, which may dramatically influence the value, any details that indicate reduced utility should be included in the description as a matter of course. The appraiser should have the skill to diplomatically specify utility-reducing details without making specifically derogatory comments about the piece.

Two period calling card cases may be entirely comparable in material, design, execution, and workmanship but if one of them has a dimension that precludes it from holding standard size business cards while the other is large enough, or even slightly overlarge for carrying modern business cards the difference in utility is obvious. The appraiser must carefully indicate the **interior** dimensions of the case of less utility, and may choose to specify in the report on the case of greater utility that it is "suitable for carrying modern business cards."

Authenticity
Authenticity means reliability, trustworthiness or genuineness.

All statements of identity by the appraiser should be based upon information that has been authenticated as far as is reasonably possible. Appropriate examination and/or testing should be performed to validate conclusions of identity and component composition. Standard gemmological tests should be employed to authenticate the identity of gemstones. Appropriate research should be undertaken to confirm the reliability of significant provenance.

Results of examination, testing, and research should be recorded on the work sheet to be maintained in the appraiser's files. The appraiser can then be prepared to give evidence in defence of an expert opinion embodied in an appraisal document.

Metals

Any test done on metal to ascertain the metal quality must be, to some extent, destructive. Touchstone testing will leave a small flat spot on the item of jewellery where metal was removed for acid testing. Electrochemical testing will leave a spot of tarnish on the surface of the tested item, which may then require polishing to remove. If quality stamps and maker's marks are clear and believable the appraiser may choose to describe metal quality as indicated by the markings. It is important for the appraisal document to clearly indicate whether or not metal testing was performed.

Metal qualities should be reported using standard conventions with due consideration of legal requirements regarding reporting the qualities of precious metals in the relevant jurisdiction. The appraiser should have a copy of and understand the rules regarding reporting of precious metal fineness for the relevant jurisdiction, and abide by them.

It is recommended that the appraiser report gold fineness using karat number conventions and spelled with a *k*, reserving carat for gemstone weights even though this spelling is sometimes used for metal fineness.

In Canada (as in USA and most jurisdictions) it is not mandatory to mark the quality of precious metals, but any mark which is an indication of the fineness of a precious metal must be factual and must be accompanied by a registered trademark unless the article is hallmarked in accordance with the laws of the United Kingdom or bears the assay mark of a foreign country which is recognised by the Canadian Department of Industry.

The prescribed (not mandatory) markings for precious metals in Canada are:
- **Gold**
  A numeral from 9 to 24 inclusive followed by "karat", "carat", "Karat", "Carat", "Kt", "Ct", "K", or "C" to indicate how many parts by weight out of twenty-four are pure gold or, alternatively, a decimal designation with a decimal point followed by three significant digits to indicate how many thousandth parts by weight are pure gold.

- Silver

  "silver", "sterling silver", "sterling", "argent", "argent sterling", or any abbreviation thereof such as "ster.", or "STG"; or the decimal format ".925" for an article which contains at least 925 parts pure silver in 1,000.

- Platinum

  "platinum", "plat.", or "platine" for an article which contains at least 95% platinum and/or iridium and/or ruthenium

- Palladium

  "palladium" or "pall." for an article which contains at least 95% palladium or 90% palladium accompanied by an additional 5% of any combination of platinum, iridium, ruthenium, rhodium, osmium and/or gold.

It is important that the appraiser know the law related to precious metal marking for the relevant jurisdiction because the rules are not internationally rationalized. There are jurisdictions where 9K is not the lowest allowed fineness of karat gold. In the UK with few exceptions the hallmarking of precious metals is mandatory.

Describing stones

The appraiser should, as far as is reasonably possible, test the identity of all materials. Guesswork and unfounded assumptions camouflaged by jargon will inevitably lead to serious errors and problems. One should never hesitate to recognise the limits of one's own knowledge and ability and when in doubt as to proper identification of material the appropriate thing to do is seek advice or even sub-contract some of the identification work. In cases where economics, time constraints, mount style, or other limiting conditions do not allow proper identification the appraiser may be obliged to make some assumptions to perform a valuation. In all such cases each assumption should be gemmologically defensible as an expert opinion and should be openly declared to be an assumption.

There should be individual detailed description of each major gemstone (only well matched major stones should be grouped together) and descriptions of the minor stones in each item. For approved gemmological species and variety names see the latest lists from the International Confederation of Jewellery, Silverware, Diamonds, Pearls and Stones (CIBJO).

Identification

Name

The name of any species or variety of gemstone used without qualification in reference to a general category of gemstones should always mean stones of natural or of cultured origin.

Diamond

The word *diamond* by itself without qualification in reference to a cut stone must always mean naturally occurring near colourless diamond fashioned in one piece into a cut stone, and otherwise unaltered by man.

Colour enhancement by irradiation and/or heat treatment, lasering, inclusion filling, coatings, assemblages of two or more pieces, any other treatment, or synthetic origin must be included as part of the identification of such diamonds.

The name of any species or variety of gemstone used without qualification in reference to a single gemstone or single set of gemstones should conform to the rules set out in nomenclature adopted by the International Confederation of Jewellery, Silverware, Diamonds, Pearls and Stones (CIBJO) and ***excludes***:
- synthetic materials,
- cultured materials,
- imitation materials, and
- assemblages of two or more pieces.

In addition the unqualified name means that the material has not been treated or altered by:
- coating,
- filling,
- dyeing,
- coloured oiling,
- surface diffusion (or deep diffusion or bulk diffusion),
- any treatment that is unstable or impermanent in normal wear and maintenance,
- any treatment that produces material with special care requirements, or

o   any treatment that yields an item of significantly less value than similar appearing untreated material that is not warranted as natural.

> **Natural**: (adjective) without human intervention

When the adjective *natural* is used, there is always a presumed set of limiting conditions. When there is contention regarding natural attribution for something, the core issue will be the presumed limiting conditions.

For a collector of gem mineral specimens, the adjective *natural* has the most comprehensive meaning with the fewest limiting presumptions. It is presumed that the sample of gem material is no longer in its original macro-environment because it obviously did not come into existence mounted in the collector's display case. The temperature, pressure, and composition of fluids adjacent to the specimen may differ markedly from the conditions in which it resided before it was collected. The solid microenvironment must be original throughout the complete specimen, however, for the attribution *natural* to apply. For the majority of mineral specimens, natural attribution requires that nothing was removed, added, repaired or in any way altered. The gem material must be in its original contact with the host matrix. In a few cases a small relaxing of requirements would allow that the specimen may still be termed natural even though some original material was removed by a process of cleaning that removed loose or water soluble surface material. Removal of coatings or other original material using solvents or reagents would, in most instances, invalidate natural status for a mineral specimen.

For a collector of gem crystals, the adjective *natural* presumes that the sample of gem material need no longer be in physical contact with original host matrix for the attribution *natural* to apply. Natural attribution still requires that nothing was added, repaired or in any way altered however. All external specimen surfaces must be in original condition and unaltered by man, with the sole exception of an induced cleavage or fracture surface developed to free the crystal from its original location.

For a gemstone, the adjective *natural* presumes the sample of gem material need no longer possess the original external surfaces for the attribution *natural* to apply. Natural attribution still requires that nothing was added, however, and all composition, structure and properties of the specimen remain in their original condition, unaltered by man.

Mechanical alteration of the exterior (i.e. cutting, polishing and/or drilling) of a gemstone, to make it easier to wear and/or to show its properties to best advantage, does not invalidate the terminology because such surface working facilitates the display of the object's properties while the composition, structure and properties are otherwise unaltered. In reference to a cut, carved or drilled gemstone *natural* means of naturally occurring substance that is in one piece and is entirely unaltered by man except for the removal of material required to alter its shape or to polish it and make it suitable for personal adornment or display.

Years ago, when synthetic gems first appeared, the question "Is it natural?" in reference to a gemstone was understandably presumed to be a request for information about origin. It was assumed the full query the questioner intended was "Is it of natural origin or is it man-made?" Basil Anderson's concern was "...namely, is the stone natural or synthetic?"[9] Robert Shipley's definition was "natural stone. A stone that occurs in nature; as distinguished from a man-made substitute..."[10]. This presumption of origin as the issue of concern addressed by the adjective *natural* has lead to this word being used as jargon in the jewellery industry to mean "not synthetic".

Nowadays, a knowledgeable person in the trade looking at a D colour diamond might similarly ask "Is it natural?" in a request for information about condition. In this case the full query the questioner intends is "Is it natural, or HTHP (high temperature / high pressure) treated?" This example of "colour enhancement" makes it clear that the adjective 'natural' is context-sensitive as far as limiting presumptions are concerned. We are now in a situation where changes in technology have produced a case within the industry where a widely accepted standard limiting presumption (that gave rise to a jargon label) is refuted by a contrary presumption. In the modern context it is clear to knowledgeable people in the trade that, contrary to the '40's presumption of what was significant,

[9] Anderson, B. W., 1947. *Gem Testing*, 4th edition, chapter VI opening paragraph.
[10] Shipley, R. M., 1945. *Dictionary of Gems And Gemology*, 2nd edition. Gemological Institute of America, Los Angeles, p. 148.

the possibility of HTHP treatment makes the D colour suspect and condition is the germane point, not origin.

In addition, public knowledge and awareness about treatments applied to gems has changed over the years, causing the issue of condition to become a significant concern to the man on the street.

When unqualified, the adjective should refer to **both** origin and condition. Whenever *natural* is used in a more limited sense, such as regarding origin but not condition or regarding condition but not origin, it should be suitably qualified to clearly indicate the limitations. An example of such a suitably qualified description is "*natural colour slightly off-round black cultured pearls...*" where the origin is not natural but the colour has not been artificially altered. Similarly, "*a ruby of natural origin*" will serve where the intent of the description is to confirm the origin while refraining from stating the condition to allow that the ruby may (or may not) be heat-treated.

It follows from the above definition and discussion that any description that includes the unqualified adjective natural in reference to a stone that has undergone any treatment, enhancement, assemblage, or synthesis is self-contradictory. Do not speak of "diffusion treated natural sapphire", "re-crystallized natural ruby", or "clarity enhanced natural emerald", for example.

One might ask why a hole drilled in a pearl with a mechanical drill should be considered any differently than a hole drilled in a diamond with a laser. A drill hole in a pearl was required to alter its shape so it could be strung or mounted. A laser-drilled hole in a diamond was not required to polish it, alter its shape, or to mount it.

The name of any gemstone species or variety applied to one stone (or set of stones) and described as "natural" should mean the indicated stone **is warranted to be** a single piece of naturally occurring substance that may have been fashioned by removal of material and/or polishing, but otherwise is entirely unaltered by man, regardless of conventional trade practice for similar such stones not specified as natural.

To identify as "sapphire" blue corundum that is not synthetic and has not undergone diffusion treatment, coating, dying or cavity filling, could be correctly describing a stone while abstaining from comment on whether or not it has undergone heat treatment. Should circumstances indicate that a qualifying adjective would be helpful to reinforce that the stone is not synthetic, one may say "genuine sapphire" although the word genuine would be redundant. Do not use the adjective natural to mean "not synthetic" because natural means much more. The words genuine, real, and true have a broad enough meaning that they may be used in a context where they can mean "not synthetic", but calling something "natural sapphire" means that, if no one else has done so, whoever has used the term guarantees that the specified stone **has undergone no treatment by man other than recovery from its place of natural occurrence, cutting, and polishing**.

Many gemstones are treated by methods which are stable and permanent, and that have been altered by processes that may be undetectable or can be neither confirmed nor refuted by standard gemmology techniques. Aquamarine and blue topaz are examples of stones which it would be unwise to described as natural because it cannot be known, except perhaps by provenance, that stones without diagnostically conclusive evidence of treatment are really of untreated colour.

It is strongly recommended that frivolous or gratuitous use of the adjective *natural* be carefully screened out of any document the appraiser produces.

Terminology used in so-called "disclosures" about stones that are not, are no longer, or never were natural varies widely. It is to be expected that vendors want to present their products in the best possible light, but the appraiser should be providing useful information to the final consumer, not sales literature for the vendor.

The following definitions and explanations are recommended for use by the appraiser in presenting information. They were written from the perspective of the every-day meaning of the words to the consumer.

These definitions will differ from jargon adopted by some segments of the gemstone industry as sales tools that purport to be terms of disclosure. Even if you understand and are comfortable with jargon terms used within the gem industry, do not use jargon in appraisals because it will not be understood by the uninitiated man on the street, and may be seriously misleading.

Treated

> **Treated**: (adjective) with properties[11] or condition[12] or composition[13] or structure[14] altered by an external agency through human intervention.

This is a blanket term for all human alterations except removal of material required to alter its shape or polish it to make it suitable for personal adornment or display.

Ethical trade practice would require full disclosure of any treatment that is unstable or impermanent in normal wear and maintenance, any treatment that produces material with special care requirements, or any treatment that yields an item of significantly less value than similar appearing untreated material that is not warranted as natural.

There are a wide variety of methods of treating stones to make them more attractive. In some instances, treatment alters a stone that deserved to be considered a gem before treatment, but improves some quality of the stone to make it even more valuable (such as most ruby and sapphire). In other cases treatment produces stones suitable for use as gems from material of marginal quality (such as blue topaz or tanzanite), thus increasing the quantity of gems available as well as providing less expensive attractive stones.

Enhanced

> **Enhanced**: (adjective) with ability, performance or quality intensified or improved by interaction with external conditions through human intervention.

A sub-category of treated, enhanced is generally considered to be less intrusive and more desirable. *Enhanced* is a friendlier sounding term than

---

[11] E.g.: colour added, changed, or deleted.
[12] E.g.: inclusions absorbed into clarified amber.
[13] E.g.: trace elements diffused into corundum.
[14] E.g.: metamict zircon heat-treated to crystalline.

treated, so is much preferred by vendors. Human intervention that improves a specific colour, such as heating to purify the blue colour of aquamarine, or the red colour of ruby, or the blue colour of sapphire, can be considered to have enhanced the colour.

An act of human intervention that produces colour in material that was naturally colourless, such as irradiated blue topaz, should not be said to yield a colour-enhanced stone. Clearly, one cannot enhance something that does not exist, and the final colour was not improved by the intervention, it was created. Similarly, an intervention that changes a colour to a different hue, such as heating amethyst to green prasiolite, should not be termed colour enhancement because the colour was entirely changed. Tanzanite is a more significant example of heat treatment that has radically changed a colour (from brown to violet-blue) so should not be termed enhanced.

The term *enhanced should be used judiciously for only the most innocuous treatments. Better to use the term treated than be seen as an apologist for the sellers of significantly altered stones.*

Cultured

> **Cultured**: (adjective) produced by a biological process with human intervention influencing the location of production.

Cultured pearls are an important part of the jewellery industry, but it would be inappropriate to require that the word *cultured* can only be applied to cultured pearls. Conceivably, someone might produce true cultured coral or any other organic gem material. It is extremely unlikely, however, that someone could find or invent a biological process that would produce gem material that in nature is inorganic. One should not speak of "cultured emerald", for example, in reference to synthetic material regardless of how much "jardin" appears to be growing inside it.

Synthetic

> **Synthetic**: (adjective) having the same structure and essentially the same composition as the naturally occurring material, but produced through human intervention from component materials.

One acceptable minor variation in composition may be a proportion of one component that is outside the expected range for the natural material, such as the higher proportion of oxygen in much flame fusion synthetic spinel. Another acceptable minor variation in composition may be absence of a component material that is detrimental to gem quality in the natural material, such as absence of water in synthetic opal because water content at over 3% in opal can produce spontaneous crazing as the material dries out.

Man-made

> **Man-made**: (adjective) produced through human intervention from component materials and may have a composition/structure not readily found in nature.

Some materials produced by man do not occur in nature, so it would not be correct to call them synthetic. Such things as YAG, GGG, or cubic zirconia[15] can be termed man-made, which is more all encompassing and may include synthetic materials as a subset).

Imitation

> **Imitation**: (adjective) a substitute for the real thing with a superficially similar appearance.

The issue as to whether something is an imitation centres upon what it is being presented as. If it is being presented accurately according to its composition, origin, and condition then it is not an imitation.

For example a plastic pendant set with faceted glass is not an imitation. It is a piece of costume jewellery that has been accurately described. If it is presented as a topaz jewel, however, the glass is imitation topaz and the plastic is imitation gold.

Imitation need not always mean glass or plastic, but may be a manmade product (e.g. cubic zirconia as imitation diamond), a synthetic

---

[15] Cubic zirconia has been found in nature as an inclusion in gem material but not as pieces large enough to cut into stones.

gemstone (e.g. synthetic ruby as imitation garnet), a treated gemstone (e.g. irradiated topaz as imitation aquamarine), or even a natural gemstone of a differing species (e.g. unheated citrine as imitation topaz).

Shape

Gemstones occur in many different shapes and may be cut in many different ways. Some cut stones do not have a discernable top and bottom and may have a name associated with their shape, such as *cube* or *rondel*, while *bead* is generally presumed to describe a fully drilled-through spherical shape (unless another shape name is added). A name for three-dimensional shapes that have a distinct top and bottom (example briolette) is rare. For most cut stones, the shape (or **outline shape**) is the shape of the shadow cast by overhead illumination onto the stone held right side up by invisible means. If the outline shape is circular then describing the shape as round is usual. Shapes other than round include oval, pear shape, marquise (or navette), triangle, square, rectangle, octagon, antique cushion and many others such as half-moon, horse's head, butterfly, and letters of the alphabet (see **gemstone shapes in the appendix**).

Except for *baguette*, which is always step cut, it should be understood that shape does not necessarily indicate the style of cut. A faceted briolette, for example, usually has rows of triangular facets but may also be step cut with trapezoid facets, or spiral cut with rhomboid facets.

Style of cut

The round brilliant style of cut is the most common for diamond, mixed cut is most common for faceted coloured stones, and cabochons are used for phenomenal and opaque stones, but many other styles of cut are also encountered (see styles of cut in the appendix).

Brilliant, Swiss, single, step, profile, rose and other styles of cut may be seen in outline shapes other than round. The name of a style of cut alone does not necessarily indicate the shape except for emerald cut which is always an octagonal step cut (sometimes also called cut-corner rectangle, cut-corner square, or trap cut). Round would be assumed for styles of cut that produce a circular shape unless another shape is specified. For example *brilliant cut* always means *round brilliant cut* unless it is accompanied by the name of another shape (such as "oval brilliant cut" or "brilliant cut marquise shape").

Number

When counting the gemstones in an item, group the count so that those counted in each group are of the same qualities, size, and cut, or are at least of appropriate sizes and qualities to all be found within the same wholesale parcel of gemstones. Provide a full description for each group of stones.

Dimensions

Two outline dimensions and the depth of individual gemstones should be measured in millimetres to the greatest level of accuracy possible given the limits of the mount and measuring device(s) used. Consider the definition of all dimensions as would be measured between parallel jaws of a measuring device. Thickness is the exception, which would be measured from point to point.

The length of a necklace, belt, bracelet, or other articulating **object**, should be measured with the item hanging vertically by one end when possible. The length of such an article should include all knots, spacers, attachments and clasps.

The length of a strand of pearls or beads should be between the outside surfaces of the end pearls and include any internal knots, spacers, and attachments but exclude anything beyond the end pearls of the strand. Do not include the knot on the outside end of the strand, if there is one, and do not include the attachment mechanism holding the strand to the clasp. Consider such attachment mechanisms and spacer knots to be related to the clasp rather than to the strand. In the case of a multi-strand necklace the shortest strand can be measured while hung vertically from one end, but set the length of a longer strand as the total of the dimensions from each end to an intermediate reference point when the article is alternately suspended vertically from each end.

For all the dimensions, the number of decimal places quoted should indicate the level of precision. When measuring a stone with a bench micrometer that gives repeatable millimetre measurements to two decimal places, or if measuring with a Leveridge gauge and estimating the second decimal place, state all dimensions to two places of decimal even when the last numeral is zero. For example write "8.30 - 8.32 x 5.00mm" not "8.3 - 8.32 x 5mm".

Specify any dimensions that are estimated and refrain from indicating more significant digits than measurement accuracy or estimation allows. The only exception to this rule (of number format being tied to level of precision) is when reporting carat weight. This will be discussed in a later section (p79).

When quoting numbers to show a range of variation always state the smallest limit of the range first followed by the largest limit of the range. It helps to consistently use the same dimension-reporting format. The following is particularly recommended for concise completeness.

- o Minimum diameter to maximum diameter by depth
- o Minimum width to maximum width by depth
- o Length by width by depth (by thickness if necessary)
- o Height by width by depth
- o Base by altitude by depth
- o Length of necklace, length of each strand if more than one.

Round

(Stones with circular outline shape): minimum diameter to maximum diameter by depth.

To indicate the range of sizes in a group of round faceted stones or cabochons quote at least the minimum diameter of the smallest and the minimum diameter of the largest.

To describe the size of a single round pearl or bead indicate its minimum and maximum diameter.
When citing a single dimension as the diameter of a pearl that dimension should be the minimum diameter.

To indicate the range of sizes in a group of round pearls quote at least the minimum diameter of the smallest and the minimum diameter of the largest.

Oval

Oval and most other shapes: length by width by depth.

For irregular shapes length is the greatest of the outline dimensions, width is the outline dimension 90° to the length or is the next largest dimension 90° to the length (see Figure 1), and **depth** is the dimension 90° to both length and width. To fully report the dimensions of a very baroque pearl such as a cultured freshwater pearl with a cupped shape of irregular outline, it may be necessary to also specify **thickness** which is the shortest point to point distance between two surfaces.

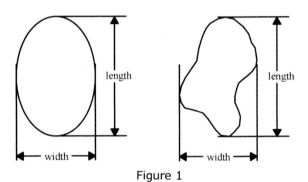

Figure 1

Symbol

Heart, letter or other symbol: height by width by depth.

Height is the top to bottom dimension of a symbol standing vertically in its typical orientation with the parallel jaws of the measuring device horizontally above and below it, width is the left/right dimension 90° to the height (see Figure 2 and Figure 3), and depth is the front to back dimension 90° to both height and width.

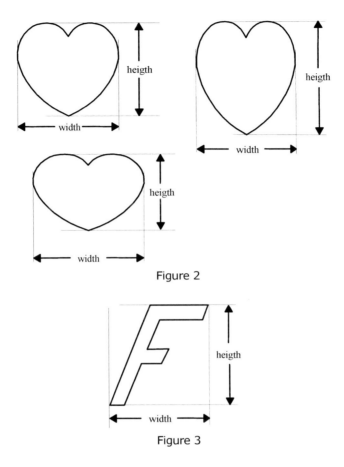

Figure 2

Figure 3

Triangle

Including shapes approximately triangular with curved sides: base by altitude by depth.

Base is the dimension along the one side of a triangle that is of greatest difference in length compared to the other two. If there are not two sides of comparable length, use the length of the longest side. Altitude is the distance from the base to the opposite point (see Figure 4); depth is 90° to both base and altitude. If a triangle is equilateral, base and depth will suffice and when only one dimension is given it is assumed to be one side (i.e. the base) of an equilateral triangle.

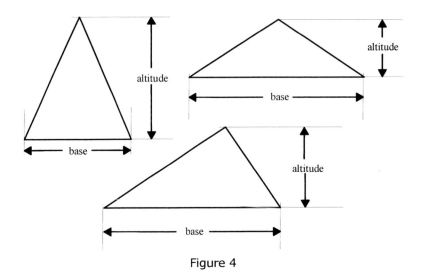

Figure 4

Hexagon

Regular (or approximately regular) shapes with an even number of edges so that opposite edges are more or less parallel: minimum width to maximum width by depth.

Pentagon

Regular (or approximately regular) shapes with an odd number of edges so that each edge is more or less opposite a vertex: minimum altitude to maximum altitude by depth

Nominal sizes

Stones that are cut to sizes suitable for setting in production-run mounts of standard dimension may be said to have the **nominal size** of that mount. The nominal size of a stone is not the dimensions of the stone but the dimensions of the standard mount into which it may be set without obvious distortion of the mount.

There may be significant variation among stones of the same nominal size because the malleability of jewellery metals allows the standard mount to be adjusted to accommodate the differences. The actual dimensions of a stone said to be of a nominal size should be within one half the difference between that nominal size and the next nominal size for that shape of stone, or should be within 1.0 mm of the nominal size, whichever is less. Describe nominal sizes without specifying units such as "an 18 x 13 (nominal size) oval rhodonite cabochon" or "a nominal 10 x 8 emerald cut blue topaz" or append the nominal size to the report of actual stone dimensions [e.g. "measuring 10.1 x 7.8 x 4.8mm (nominal 10 x 8)"].

Groups of stones

Groups of similar small gemstones (i.e. they would be found in a whole-sale parcel of stones being offered at the same price per carat for any or all stones in the parcel) may have their sizes indicated by the range of out-line dimensions of the stones.

Carat weight

The weights of individual gemstones, or the total weight of a group of gemstones, should be expressed in carats (symbol ct) to **always two** and **only two** decimal places. It is appropriate to quote carat weight to three decimal places as additional information or clarification appended to the official two decimal place carat weight. For example "weighing by scale $1.00^{(0.999)}$ carat" or "weighing by scale $1.00^{(1.004)}$ carat" is acceptable, but the **official** carat weight should always be to two and only two decimal places. Requirements for rounding of the carat weight vary according to jurisdiction, and it is **not** always to the nearest 0.01 ct. The International Confederation of Jewellery, Silverware, Diamonds, Pearls and Stones (CIBJO) and most diamond clubs require that the third decimal place be ignored except when it is a nine, in which case the second decimal place numeral may be rounded up. In discussing this issue of rounding with dealers in fine coloured gemstones in Toronto, New York, and London the consensus seemed to be that ignoring the third decimal place unless it is a nine would be the preferred rounding convention. This approach is recommended because it guarantees that the client will receive full measure.

The great advantage of the two-decimal-place carat convention is that it allows for very little misunderstanding of specified carat weights. By the above convention and rounding standards the stone that shows 0.025 on the weigh scale must be called 0.02 ct, which could never be mistaken for a quarter of a carat instead of a fortieth. The stone that shows 0.125 on the scale must be called 0.12 ct and so could never be mistaken for over one carat.

Specify "in total" when quoting the weight of more than one stone. Also indicate "by scale" if the stones were actually weighed, or "approximately" if estimated or if reporting a purported actual weight that was confirmed from the stone's dimensions is likely to be accurate.

This convention of reporting two decimal places for carat weight should be used **without regard to precision of weight estimation**. If using standard formulae to calculate the approximate weight of a mounted stone from its dimensions and assumed specific gravity and, after adjustments for girdle thickness, bulge factor, and crown height, the number on the calculator is 5.0429825 report "weighing approximately 5.04 carats," because this is a best effort at estimating the official two decimal place carat weight, and has been declared as an estimation.

In circumstances when it is not possible to accurately measure or make a reasonable estimation of the dimensions of a stone, "weighing approximately five carats," indicates a general approximation but if reporting in numerals specify two decimal places according to the convention.

When the weight of a stone is on the cusp between two price groups it must be established which price group is being worked with to set the value. Undoubtedly the stone "weighing approximately 5.04 carats" may just as easily have an actual weight of 4.96 ct or 5.12 ct, and the 4.96 ct stone would have a lower per carat value. The job of appraiser is to formulate an opinion. A report that says "weighing approximately 5.04 ct" clearly indicates which price group was assumed. A report saying "approximately five carats" and offering a single value may leave doubt about which price group was used and the opinion is less rigorous. It would be better to add "the valuation assumes a full five carats" than to leave it unclear. **Do not** ever use an average between price groups for weight ranges, a stone is either in one weight range or the next, not half way between the two. The alternative to choosing one or the other is to report "approximately five carats" and offer two values, one for short of five carats, the other for a full five-carat stone.

Do not put a period after *ct* or pluralize it. Consider *ct* to be a symbol. As a symbol it requires neither pluralization nor special punctuation.

Furthermore, do not pluralize the word carat unless the weight quoted is equal to or greater than 1.01 ct even if the third decimal place would show a weight greater than unity. Acceptable examples would be "2.18 carats", "2.18 ct", "1.01 ct", "1.01 carats" or "1.00 (1.008) carat". Note that "0.13 carats" is quite unacceptable, as is "1.00 carats"; while "2.18 cts" indicates a lack of understanding about use of symbols with the redundant "s".

Always place a zero before the decimal point of a carat weight when the weight is less than 1.00 carat (e.g. not ".27 ct" but rather "0.27 ct").

It has become conventional throughout the jewellery industry that carat weights of less than one carat may be spoken of as a one or two digit numeral expressed in words and followed by the word *point(s)* to indicate that these numerals in the carat weight are to the right of the decimal point. For example a stone weighing 0.21 ct may be said to be a twenty-one point stone or 0.07 ct may be referred to as seven points. This results from the curious difference between written and spoken language when discussing numbers. "A twenty-one point stone" is quicker and easier to say than "a stone weighing zero point two one carat", while "0.21 ct" is quicker and easier to write. Similarly "seven points" is much quicker and easier to say than "zero point zero seven carat" while "0.07 ct" is quicker and easier to write. In each of these cases the information conveyed is a clear unambiguous representation of the carat weight of each stone. The word *point* in each case refers to the ***decimal point*** in the carat weight and ***not*** to ***another unit*** of weight. We are always talking about carat weight, not "point weight". This is quite clear if someone says "The carat weight is twelve points."

In discussing carat weight **the word *point* should _not_ be** abbreviated in text and should be in combination with the number section of the carat weight **in word format** only, ***not numerals*** (e.g.: write "0.12 ct" or "twelve points" but **not** "12 points", nor "0.12 points", nor "0.12 pt.", nor "twelve pt.").

The reason this use of the word *point* works so well and is not misunderstood is because of the two and only two decimal place convention for carat weight. To the right of the decimal point there are always two digits. Misunderstanding develops only when "point" is considered a unit of weight rather than a way of expressing the carat weight verbally.

Years ago there was a national Canadian newspaper advertisement that had jewellers telephoning one another to ask if they had seen "that crazy ad for half carat diamond ear studs at a ridiculous price". What the advertising offered was a pair of "0.50 pt total weight" diamond ear studs. The vendor claimed that there was nothing misleading about his special sale because all the items he was selling contained well in excess of the advertised total weight of half a point. One pair of those "earrings" seen by the author contained two "promotional" quality (i.e. rejection quality that would take a lot of promoting to sell to anyone) single cut diamonds weighing in total approximately three points set in gold plated base metal. Remember this sheer nonsense of "fifty points of a point" as a reminder that *point* is not a unit of weight, it is a way of expressing carat weight in words. Get the point!

Extremely small diamonds are a nomenclature nuisance and are rarely encountered singly in articles of jewellery worthy of being appraised. If a diamond weighing under 0.01 ct must be described specify that the weight is **"less than 0.01 carat"**, additional details of weight being neither required nor prohibited, but better left unspecified.

For information and calculation purposes small diamond melee information may be recorded on the work sheet in a fraction format with the numerator being the number of stones and the denominator how many of them it would take to make up a full carat of weight. Any written report, however, should specify the total weight of a given number of like stones in standard two-decimal-place format. As an example, given six diamonds, forty of which would weigh one carat, record on the work sheet 6/40 ct and report six diamonds weighing in total 0.15 carat. Twelve mounted single cut diamonds each being 0.9 mm in diameter could be recorded as "12/240 ct 8/8" and reported as twelve single cut diamonds weighing in total approximately 0.05 carat. In the latter case "8/8" is a short hand way of writing *single cut*[16], the style of cut having eight main facets above and eight main facets below the girdle.

When reporting on similar stones in a group, **don't** give the count and the weight of **one** of the stones. <u>Give the **count** and *total* **weight of all the stones together.**</u>

The total-weight approach means that one diamond weighing $0.20^{(0.206)}$ ct together with a matching diamond weighing $0.20^{(0.208)}$ ct is described as two diamonds having a total weight of 0.41 ct, which is more accurate than 0.20 ct (according to the rounding rule) each. This eliminates temptation to specify carat weight of small melee in (foolish and) undesirable "fractions-of-a-point"!

Stones that are considered separately to arrive at a perceived cost should be individually described with the weight of each individual stone reported. For example, say *"a pair … ear studs … containing one brilliant cut diamond … weighing approximately 0.20 ct, of E-F colour, VS clarity, and good make; and one brilliant cut diamond … weighing approximately 0.20 ct, of H-I colour, SI clarity, and good make."*

It is better to avoid using fraction format (such as "half carat") to describe carat weight. If there is some reason to prefer using such a format to describe the weight of gemstones be sure that the weight of the reported stone(s) will meet or exceed the equivalent decimal carat weight notation.

The weight of mounted stones can be estimated with reasonable accuracy if precise measurements are taken.

The formulae for calculating diamond weights employ a constant and the physical dimensions. The formulae for calculating the weights of other gemstones use the specific gravity of the gem material together with the

---

[16] Interestingly, this is a parallel case of the difference between written and spoken language in discussing numbers. When notes are read, the shorthand 8/8 is more likely to be verbalized by knowledgeable people in the trade as "eight cut" than as "single cut" or "eight over eight" because it has fewer syllables while conveying the precise meaning.

dimensions and a constant to arrive at an estimate of weight. There are different formulae for differing outline shapes. See the tables of weight estimation formulae in the appendix.

With stones cut in other than round brilliant style, an adjustment (sometimes called a "fudge factor" involving a percentage of increase or decrease) may have to be used to allow for variations in shape and proportions.

It can be a very useful exercise to check the accuracy of weight estimations from formulae when handling loose stones. By estimating the weight from dimensions and then comparing to actual carat weight, one can see the "fudge factor" needed to bring calculated weight to agree with the scale weight and take note of which proportions of the stone have made that adjustment necessary

Grading diamonds

The marketing of diamonds has more or less established the universality of "*the four C's*" of colour, clarity, cut, and carat weight as the factors influencing the cost and value of gemstones. We have discussed carat weight, so now on to the others.

Colour

A simple description of the colour of near colourless diamonds, such as "good" or "fine" or "poor" is entirely unacceptable.

There are colour grading systems recognized by the American Gem Society (AGS), Gemological Institute of America (GIA), International Diamond Council (IDC), Diamond High Council (HRD), International Confederation of Jewellery, Silverware, Diamonds, Pearls and Stones (CIBJO), and Scandinavian Diamond Nomenclature (Scan.DN), which relate to one another as well as to historical colour names and which are understood world wide. The GIA diamond colour grading system is most frequently referenced by the systems which refer to another, and is the grading terminology which predominates in North America for grading near colourless diamonds because it is the most widely understood. The appraiser should recognize all of these systems, be able to translate between them (see the cross reference chart p167), and do diamond grading in one of them using certificated diamonds as colour grading master stones.

When grading a loose diamond specify one single colour grade because the job of a diamond grader is to decisively assign a grade to the stone. The person who bracket-grades a loose diamond either does not understand what is required for grading a diamond or is indicating that limiting conditions prevented them from doing a proper grading job. If this is the case those limiting conditions should be clearly specified in accompaniment to the bracketed colour grade. If the intention in naming two colour grades for one loose stone was to indicate that the stone is on the cusp between those two grades, it would be correct to assign one or other grade to the stone and indicate as additional information that it is on the border line with the other grade. For example one might grade a stone as "colour G (borderline F)" or "colour F (borderline G)". Just naming two colour grades for one loose diamond is wrong, period.

Bracketing of colour grades is acceptable and recommended only when grading a set diamond. In this circumstance one should bracket the colour grading over at least two grades because the limiting condition of having a set stone precludes grading the stone to the highest level of accuracy. When grading a diamond set in yellow gold bracket the colour over at least three grades because how much of the colour seen is reflected from the setting cannot be known and, of course, point out this limiting condition in the report (e.g. "grading accuracy is influenced by the yellow gold setting"). When reporting the grading on a group of diamonds indicate the range of colour grades across the group not just the average. In addition to being more precise this also indicates how well matched the colours are.

If an employer imposes some other diamond colour grading system (such as an in-house grading system), provide a translation from the other system to one of the recognized systems.

Diamonds of fancy colour (defined by the limit of each of the near-colourless diamond colour grading systems) should have their colour described in terms of purity, tone, and hue, as should all coloured gemstones. See *Grading coloured gemstones* p89.

Clarity

A simple description such as "good" is every bit as unacceptable in describing clarity as it would be for colour.   A clarity grade must be specified.

The clarity grade designations which have evolved for diamonds, FL, IF, VVS, VS, SI, and I, are used world wide except that the lowest grade may be termed I (for included) or P (for piqué).

Settings that hold a stone securely must cover some parts of the stone and hide some of the interior from view. It therefore cannot be ascertained if a mounted diamond is in fact internally flawless (IF grade) or flawless (FL grade). If no inclusion whatever can be seen in a mounted diamond the appraiser can only presume the clarity grade; indeed that is part of the job of the appraiser if an opinion of value is to be formulated.   Whatever presumption is made and used as the basis for valuation should be specified on the appraisal and clearly stated to be a presumption. It would be prudent to more often presume VVS clarity but "presumed IF" or even "presumed FL" could be valid. It is not beyond the bounds of reason to offer the client a choice between the alternative presumptions, although this approach would be rare and all possibilities of abuse should be very carefully considered long before the subject is broached with the client.

The clarity grades of VVS, VS, SI, and I (or P) are routinely subdivided into VVS_1, VVS_2, VS_1, VS_2, SI_1, SI_2, I_1, I_2 and I_3 for larger sizes.   The expectations of some retailers, members of the insurance industry and consumers have tended to influence appraisers to apply the sub-grades to ever-smaller diamonds. This has become so much the case that diamond clarity sub-grades are approaching being as much a long-standing joke as the story of the old diamond dealer who says, "Oh sure, the weather is very nice; but is that very nice one, or very nice two?"

One should be reasonable in the use of clarity sub-grades. Some say that the sub-grades should not be used on diamonds smaller than 0.47 carat, yet in North America it has become usual to sub-grade the clarity of diamonds larger than 0.22 carat when they are the major stone(s) in an item.   It makes no sense to use sub-grades on, as examples, a 0.05 ct diamond or on old European cut diamonds that are priced as old stones.

At least the old diamond dealer did not ask if the weather was "very nice three", which is a completely different joke.

It is not recommended to use the "SI_3" pseudo-grade. Make the decision as to whether the stone is SI_2 or I_1 and if it's a tough call then go ahead and be tough, you can do it! To some people "SI_3" has the appearance of a rather crass attempt to flog more low-end goods by watering down the grading standards. This may be unfairly impugning the motives of its proponents. As it has been presented, "SI_3" would actually be narrowing the standards for the lower clarity grades. The theory is that "SI_3" includes the lowest of what was previously called SI_2 together with the best of what was previously called I_1. This narrows the range for SI_2 and for I_1 while placing a new grade between them.

The difficulty is that "SI_3" is not universally accepted. The marketer of an SI_2 near the low end of this range is unlikely to eagerly accept having that stone relabelled "SI_3", while the marketer of an I_1 stone would be expected to look with favour upon having that stone labelled "SI_3". When different standards are being used by different graders, prospective purchasers tend to assume that stones offered for sale as SI_2 were more likely graded by someone using the standard in place before the introduction of "the SI_3 grade" while stones marketed as "SI_3" would have been graded I_1 by those standards.

Regardless of the motives of the "SI_3" proponents, the reality of the marketplace influences the grading standards such that a stone offered for sale graded "SI_3" would almost always be an upgraded piqué stone. It is better to maintain the original SI_2 and I_1 standards.

Make

The one quality that is most often overlooked or glossed over when diamonds and coloured stones are being described is make. It is cut, the last of the "four C's", and refers to the quality of workmanship done by the cutter including shape, proportions, symmetry, polish, and details of finish such as sharpness of facet edges, "pointing-up" of the facets and roughness of the girdle.

The term make is preferable to the word cut in this context because it cannot be misunderstood to mean style of cut. For many there would be a clear understanding of the difference between the questions "What is the cut?" and "How is the cut?" But "What is the cut?" and "How is the make?" leaves much less room for misunderstanding.

This is one of the few instances in description of gemstones where "less is more". Give a general description of the overall make of the stone, such as very good, good, medium, fair, or poor or employ a make grading system that uses such terms for make grades. Additional information about the details of the make would be optional for most cases. For important stones some details of make could be included as additional information. In the usual case where details of make are not reported, the information should just be record on the work sheet as justification for the appraiser's judgement of the overall make.

Unquestionably, proportions have a much greater influence upon quality of cut than other components of make. There is no problem with a description of a diamond that includes specific details of proportion when this provides additional information that does not mislead. It is doing the retail customer a great disservice, however, to rely on proportion percentages to convey information about make. The customer is a non-expert who will rely on the expert opinion to make decisions of consequence. For example, a description of a diamond which includes the information "*38% pavilion depth,* polished girdle, closed culet, and very good finish" would be clearly understood by anyone who knows about proportions to refer to a very poorly made fish-eye diamond, a diamond with such a shallow pavilion that much brilliance will be lost as light leaks out through the back of the stone. Such a description should be considered misleading when offered to the man on the street because a non-expert would particularly notice "very good finish" and would ignore or misunderstand the proportion percentage as somehow related to the finish, which is called "very good" even though a correct interpretation of the proportion information clearly establishes that the make is very poor!

It is unreasonable to defend such a description as more detailed than a simple "poor make". The words *very good* are emotionally loaded words that the average non-expert would particularly notice and would consider more significant than the technical meaning requires. The layperson could also misunderstand finish to be a synonym of cut in the sense of make. Even the jargon of the diamond industry refers to finished meaning cut diamonds as opposed to rough.

A description which says "of poor make with 38% pavilion depth, polished girdle, closed culet, and very good finish" is somewhat better, but it could still be misunderstood because both phrases "poor make" and "very good finish" are there, and may cause confusion.

A make grade or a simple more general description of make provides much more useful advice to the non-expert avoiding the complexities of the jargon (rough, finished, cut, make, finish) of the trade.

If one chooses to add specific details to the make grade or to a general description of the make, finish should not be mentioned unless it is poor. When the finish is good or better, it has little importance compared to the other components of make while the meaning and significance of finish specifications could be misunderstood by the person(s) who will make decisions of consequence based on their understanding of the report.

Grading coloured gemstones

In the grading of coloured gemstones a parallel may be drawn to "the four C's" used for diamonds. To indicate all the features of a coloured stone that influence its value we must specify carat weight, colour, clarity, and make.

Colour

Colour grading of coloured gemstones is very much more of an art than the colour grading of near colourless diamonds (note that fancy colour diamonds should be graded as coloured stones of the species diamond).

Colour description

Colour is the brain's interpretation of our perception of a combination of many wavelengths of light stimulating the eye. It has been considered to be subjective, making colour communication very difficult. The CIE System of 1931 is the foundation of modern colour science. Most other industries, i.e. paper, clothing, automobile, film, and television have used colour science in colour matching far more than has the jewellery industry.

Dr. James B. Nelson introduced the Nelson-Lovibond gemstone colorimeter in the Journal of Gemmology in 1986. In a prior article in 1985 on Colour Filters and Gemmological Colorimetry, Dr. Nelson points out that in 1952 M. D. S. Lewis wrote three articles on colour perception and measurement in which he advised the gemstone trade to urgently consider this "universally adopted system of colour specification and measurement as the basis of gemmological colorimetry". Lewis, in his turn, pointed out an article of September 1933 on "Measurement of the Colours of Precious Stones" with description of the Guild Trichromatic Colorimeter! It would seem past time for the jewellery industry to start using scientifically meaningful descriptions of colour.

A complete and accurate description of the appearance of a coloured gemstone would include a graph of the spectral composition of the illuminating light source and graphs of the spectral composition of light transmitted through or remitted from each spot of the stone that provides a differing colour sensation. These graphs would be repeated for varying angles of incident light and a measurement of the brightness of the light for each case would need to be provided. Such an extremely complex system of description is sheer imagination and well beyond available technology.

Scientific, instrument based, and commercial gem description systems **do not** describe the appearance of the stone. They describe one colour seen, and can do this with significant precision.

Colour scientists will maintain that a number based system must serve much better than any words to quantitatively describe colour. Such scientific colour notation as Tristimulus Co-ordinates (X, Y, Z), or chromaticity and luminance co-ordinates (x, y, Y), are obscure CIE numbers in scientifically accurate colour space notation that would not be understood by the appraisal client. Even the more comprehensible dominant wavelength, percentage excitation purity, and metric lightness numbers would confuse rather than enlighten.

It is recommended that words be used to describe the colour, if only as a preamble to scientific notation, but it is important to squeeze as much meaning into those words as possible by tying them to a defensible subtractive[17] colour mix system. Proper scientific colour notation may be particularly desirable in an expert opinion for certain cases. It is recommended, however, that when scientific (or even pseudo-scientific) colour notation is used it should not stand on its own, but be preceded by a description of colour using plain words when the report is intended for the use of a non-expert. The client can then get information he can understand and use as the basis for making significant decisions regarding the article appraised.

For any colour comparison environment or colour describing system, standardisation of the incident light is particularly important. The "near daylight" CIE source C (S_C)(=6775°K), a filtered variation of CIE source A (S_A) which is an incandescent tungsten lamp operating at 2855°K, has been an international standard. Because it is incandescent all wavelengths are produced, which is important. A diffused light source is better for colour grading than a point light source, because a point source would be more dramatic in showing optical phenomena, which would distract from observation of body colour.

Most modern commercial colour-viewing booths in the printing industry use light of colour temperature 5000° (considered to be a bit more evenly balanced with less blue emphasis than S_C) with a light intensity of about 200 foot candles and a colour rendering index of 90 to 100%. The colour-rendering index is an indication of how true colours will appear under a light source that has an imbalance in the visible spectrum. All fluorescent lights will have less than 100% colour rendering because some wavelengths they generate are much brighter than others and a graph of the visible wavelengths they produce would be very "spiky".

Most fluorescent lights are not recommended for comparing or grading colours because their limited wavelengths can generate unwanted metamerism (the extreme of which is termed colour flair in the printing and dyeing industries and is known to gemmologists as the alexandrite-like colour change). Colour flair can be quite pronounced under different

---

[17] There are two ways of producing a colour. Additive mixing, as seen in a projection type large screen colour television, adds different wavelengths of light together. Subtractive mixing, as seen when paint is mixed, combines one pigment which subtracts some wavelengths together with another pigment which again subtracts other wavelengths. This combining of wavelength subtractors is subtractive colour mixing.

fluorescent light sources of similar colour temperature, while under incandescent lights colour flair is more directly related to colour temperature.

Three important numbers that have been used to describe lighting are colour temperature, colour rendering index, and metamerism index.

Colour temperature is a comparison of the colour of the light in relation to the colour of the light that would be given off by a black body heated to the stipulated number of degrees Kelvin. At 1000°K a black body would glow dull red, at 2000°K orange-red, at 3000°K yellow, at 4000°K to 8000°K white to bluish-white, and over 8000°K the light would contain higher and higher proportions of blue, violet, and ultraviolet light.

Colour rendering index is an indication of how closely the light comes to producing the same colour sensation as an incandescent 6500°K illuminant for a standard series colour gamut[18].

Metamerism index indicates how strong the colour differences are under an incandescent 6500°K illuminant for a standard series of metamers (pairs of colour swatches which match one another under a lower colour temperature illuminant).

There are some high intensity arc lamps, originally designed for 16mm film projectors and now used for medical and surgical illumination, that provide bright (300 Watts @ 60 lumens per watt) white incandescent light at a colour temperature of 5000° K. More affordable and somewhat longer-lived are some of the quartz-halogen lights (such as the SoLux MR-16) that have a colour temperature of between 4500° and 4800° K and which are also incandescent. Some fluorescent lamps have been produced with improved colour rendering and reduced metamerism, but even though it is easier for fluorescents to produce light of higher colour temperature, the spiky nature of fluorescent light tends to yield a lower colour rendering index and higher metamerism index than incandescent lights. The appraiser should record in the notes kept on file the lighting(s) used for grading coloured gemstones.

---

[18] A colour gamut is the full collection of all colours available in a specified series of colours. A set of colour samples may be a preferentially limited gamut for a particular application. There are many sets of colour samples (or systems for precisely describing colour) that are intended to be as comprehensive as possible, but every such set (or system) will have some colours that are not included. No colour gamut is "universal".

The descriptions of colour that are yielded by commercial or scientific systems can be rather difficult to interpret. "C80, M50, Y90" would mean very little to the average person. Someone who understands some colour theory could deduce that it is a subtractive mix formula of cyan, magenta and yellow but would have difficulty visualizing it without a reference chart. "Sombre dark yellowish green" would have more meaning for someone unfamiliar with colour theory. Such a description of colour could serve on its own or be a helpful preamble to a scientific colour notation that the client would view as obscure.

Conversational colour descriptions should be based on the traditional three colour components of purity (chroma), tone (lightness) and hue.

Hue is what we normally think of when naming colours, i.e. red, green, blue, yellow and so on with intermediate hue names such as blue-green, bluish green, greenish blue, slightly bluish green etc. The hue can be indicated in scientifically defensible subtractive colour mixing terms without using quaint colour names that are open to wide interpretation.

(Hue is precisely specified by the CIE dominant wavelength number in scientific notation. It has also been reported by the CIELAB "hue angle" on the colour wheel with slightly purplish red at the 0° position to the right and consecutive colours red, orange, yellow, green and so on in counter-clockwise rotation around a colour-neutral centre; with the hue being indicated by its angular position in degrees between 0 and 360.)

Avoid "designer names" like "dusk rose"; food names like "apple green", "pumpkin" or "peach"; the floral "cornflower blue", "rhododendron red" or "rose pink"; and animal colour references such as "pigeon blood", "baby blue" and "flesh red". Use of geographic references to indicate colour (regardless of the stone's actual or purported origin) is undesirable because locations renowned as sources of the finest qualities also produce mediocre and even inferior qualities.

Tone is the location of the colour in a range of lighter to darker colours, where the colour is between the extremes of pure white and complete black. (It is precisely specified by the CIELUV metric lightness value in scientific notation.)

The adjectives best used to describe tone are **very dark**, **dark**, **medium-dark**, **medium**, **medium-light**, **light**, and **pale** (corresponding to 8 to 2 in the GIA system). Occasionally a stone encountered may be appropriately described as **very pale** (GIA tone 1) and rarely a stone may be encountered that is so very dark as to be appropriately described as **hue-black** (GIA tone 9)(e.g. blue-black).

In considering the tone grade for a colour it may be helpful to bear in mind the various tones for the hue red and consider that what we would in normal conversation consider to be the crossover between red and deep pink would be at the tone transition from medium to medium-light.

Purity (sometimes called **intensity**[19] or **saturation**) is the pureness of the colour and indicates where the colour resides between the extremes of completely neutral grey and the pure spectral hue. (It is precisely specified by the CIELUV metric chroma value in scientific notation.)

The adjectives best used to describe colour purity are **vivid, strong, substantial, mellow, sombre and dull.** These can correspond to the GIA saturation numbers 6 to 1 respectively.

In considering the purity grade of a colour, bear in mind that most good quality gems are in the substantial to strong range and vivid should only refer to colours with purity near or at that of actual rainbow colours.

Purity, tone, hue, in that order, can sound like a conversational description of a colour and still give helpful details of what the colour actually looks like.

Bear in mind that describing a colour is **not** giving the colour grade of the stone. Judgements of purity / tone / hue are colour specific, not species specific. Different gem species occur in differing ranges of colour. Imagine two stones of identically matching light blue colour: one a corundum, the other a beryl. The purity / tone / hue description should be identical in each case even though the colour grade of the sapphire could be near the bottom of the range while the same colour in the aquamarine could be near the top of the range of colour quality.

---

[19] Some colour scientists object to use of the term *intensity* for anything other than a numerical and linear (i.e. not logarithmic) quantifiable measurement.

Example descriptions: tsavolite garnet of strong medium-dark slightly yellowish green; a tourmaline of substantial medium greenish blue; ruby of vivid medium-dark red; mellow very pale slightly greenish blue aquamarine.

Colour standards

For important stones or contentious cases it is particularly helpful to have a standard reference gamut of colour samples against which individual stones (or other coloured materials such as enamel or porcelain) can be directly compared. It should be understood that there will always be colours that lie outside the range of samples of any colour gamut, no matter how comprehensive the range of samples is. The greater the number of samples in a reference set, the more frequent will be precise matches of colour and fewer will be the number of interpolations necessary due to mismatching.

The book Color Atlas by Harald Kueppers (translator: R. Marcinik, Pub. Barron's, 1982) was an inexpensive colour reference manual with pages of graduated colour squares with subtractive colour mix notation.

Unfortunately it went out of print, but any similar printed colour matrix can provide a very useful reference gamut of colours for your own files. Perhaps the ultimate such example would be the full set of colour chips in the Pantone colour series.

It is recommended that the appraiser adopt or develop a standardised approach when comparing a colour against those in a colour gamut. A square hole can be cut in a piece of white card to mask adjacent colours in the samples against which a stone is to be compared. Always compare one colour (such as a single totally reflected flash of light within a faceted stone), not the general overall appearance of the stone, against individual reference samples. If there is significant colour zoning or pleochroism, then it may be appropriate to compare and describe two, three, or more different colours seen through the top of the stone. Any description of colour(s) seen through the side, end, or back of any stone should be ancillary information clearly recognisable as supplementary information, with colour(s) seen through the top of the stone being of paramount consideration.

"GEMDIALOGUE" by Howard Rubin is his system for grading and describing coloured gems. The colour description section uses sets of excellent transparent colour filters for standard reference hues to describe colour by subtractive mixing. The colour samples, which were spiral bound in the early editions, are now in a three-ring binder that allows them to be removed and freely combined to produce wider combinations and a greater number of reference colours.

The "COLORMASTER", a colour comparison device that was introduced in 1979 by GIA, was withdrawn from the market in the spring of 1996. About five hundred of the machines were sold and it was reported[20] that the GIA will continue to service those still in operation. They use the three primary colours in somewhat cumbersome additive mixing (with some subtractive modification) to describe colours.

The "GIA colored stone grading system" is another system for grading and describing coloured gems. The colour description section uses numbers and letter-symbols (with optional word format) to specify the hue, tone, and purity of colours in a subtractive mixing description and has colour quality charts for the different gem species. They also offer moulded plastic colour sample sets.

The "Gemworld Price Guide Reference Manual" presents a good colour grading system that is somewhat similar to the GIA system but with colour quality charts indicating colour quality numbers that may differ from those proposed by the GIA.

<u>Colour grade</u>

Having described the colour, it is now necessary to judge the overall desirability of that colour. Decide where it belongs on a scale of 1 to 10 with 10 being the connoisseur's epitome of perfection for that species and variety and 1 being the lowest limit of marginal desirability. In general terms the limits are:
EXTRA FINE - 8 to 10: vivid to strong most desired hue of optimum tone with even distribution; the best colour of the variety

---

[20] *Colored Stone* magazine, volume 9-No.3-May/June 1996, p 8.

FINE - 6 to 8: slight deviation from ideal colour, perhaps slightly lighter or darker tone (still highly desirable)

GOOD - 4 to 6: farther from ideal, perhaps lighter or darker or zoned or less than strong (still desirable)

COMMERCIAL - 1 to 4: far from ideal, perhaps dull to sombre purity or pronounced zoning (marginal to acceptable desirability).

Colour quality charts

The following is a sample of some colour quality charts from the Gemworld Price Guide Reference Manual that have been modified with addition of this author's adjective labels. Each grid cross references purity and tone for specified hues of the named species and variety. There is a separate grid for all major species and varieties and some more important species and varieties may have separate grids for slightly differing hues.

	Dull	Sombre	Mellow	Sub-stantial	Strong	Vivid	Corundum (Sapphire) Blue
2	1	1.5	2.5				Pale
3	1.5	2.5	3	4	5		Light
4	2	3	4	5	6.5	8.5	Medium Light
5	2	3.5	4.5	6	7.5	9	Medium
6	2	3.5	5	6.5	8.5	10	Medium Dark
7	1.5	2	3	4	5.5		Dark
8	1	1.5	2	2.5			Very Dark
	1	2	3	4	5	6	

	Dull	Sombre	Mellow	Sub-stantial	Strong	Vivid	Corundum (Sapphire) Violetish Blue
2	1	1.5	2				Pale
3	1.5	2	3	4	5		Light
4	2	2.5	4	5	6.5	8	Medium Light
5	2	3	4.5	6	7.5	9	Medium
6	2	3.5	5	6.5	8.5	10	Medium Dark
7	1	2	3	4	5.5		Dark
8	1	1.5	2	2.5			Very Dark
	1	2	3	4	5	6	

	Dull	Sombre	Mellow	Sub-stantial	Strong	Vivid	Corundum (Sapphire) very slightly Greenish Blue
2	1	1.5	2				Pale
3	1.5	2	2.5	3.5	4		Light
4	2	2.5	3.5	4.5	6	7	Medium Light
5	2	2.5	4	5.5	6.5	8	Medium
6	2	2.5	4	5.5	6.5	8	Medium Dark
7	1.5	2	3	4	5		Dark
8	1	1.5	2				Very Dark
	1	2	3	4	5	6	

	Dull	Sombre	Mellow	Sub-stantial	Strong	Vivid	Bluish Violet
2	1	1.5	2				Pale
3	1.5	2	2.5	3	4		Light
4	2	2.5	3	4	5	6.5	Medium Light
5	2	2.5	4	5	6.5	8	Medium
6	2	2.5	3.5	5	6	7	Medium Dark
7	1.5	2	3	3.5	4.5		Dark
8	1	1.5	2	2.5			Very Dark
	1	2	3	4	5	6	

As can be seen by comparing the four sapphire charts above, differing hues within the same variety can be considered to be of significantly different colour quality even when of the same purity and tone.

The following generic colour quality charts are this author's general-purpose charts for species or varieties that are not separately provided. One is for full-range colour varieties of optimum hue, the other is for the optimum hue of varieties that do not occur in dark tones. These should be used as a general guide only when charts for the species and variety are not available.

	Dull	Sombre	Mellow	Sub-stantial	Strong	Vivid	full range colour of optimum hue
2	1	1.5	2.5				Pale
3	1.5	2	3	4	5		Light
4	2	2.5	4	5	6.5	8.5	Medium Light
5	2	3	4.5	6	7.5	9.5	Medium
6	2	3.5	5	6.5	8.5	10	Medium Dark
7	1.5	2	3	4	5.5		Dark
8	1	1.5	2	2.5			Very Dark
	1	2	3	4	5	6	

	Dull	Sombre	Mellow	Sub-stantial	Strong	Vivid	pale coloured varieties of optimum hue
1	1	1.5	2.5				Very Pale
2	1.5	2	3	4	5		Pale
3	2	2.5	4	5	6.5	8.5	Light
4	2	3	4.5	6	7.5	9	Medium Light
5	2	3.5	5	6.5	8.5	10	Medium
	1	2	3	4	5	6	

Clarity in coloured stones

Unlike diamonds, there is not one single generally accepted clarity grading system for coloured stones. For example, the GIA offers a coloured stone clarity grading system that re-defines the terms used in clarity grading of diamonds for each of three categories of coloured stones. To have four different definitions for the SI clarity grade (for example) must be very confusing to the non-expert; people in the trade have difficulty with the concept! In contrast, the American Gem Society (AGS) offers a system that provides terms for coloured stone clarity grades that entirely differ from the diamond terminology.

The American Gem Society approach is very clear and avoids confusion with the 10X diamond clarity grades. These advantages allow this approach to be very much recommended. The following clarity grading is the author's variation of this approach with split grading of the main grades and the use of 10X diamond clarity grades as sub-grades of the FI clarity grade.

Clarity grades of coloured stones are based on the visibility of inclusions without magnification. Stones that are given the FI (free-of-inclusions) grade may have the 10X clarity grade (as used for diamonds) added in parenthesis following the FI grade [e.g. "clarity grade FI (VS_2)"].

Clarity: visibility of inclusions to the trained eye under ideal lighting conditions without any magnification (the 10X clarity grade may be added in parenthesis only to those stones that have been given the FI grade).

Quality #	Type I (e.g. aquamarine)	Type II (e.g. sapphire)	Type III (e.g. emerald)	
10	FI (to VVS-1)	FI (to VS-1)	FI	free of inclusions
9	FI (VVS-2 to VS-1)	FI (VVS-2 to SI-2)	LI-1	lightly
8	FI (VS-2 to SI-1)	LI-1	LI-2 ⟩ LI	included
7	FI (SI-2)	LI-2	MI-1	moderately
6	LI-1	MI-1	MI-2 ⟩ MI	included
5	LI-2	MI-2	HI-1	heavily
4	MI-1	HI-1	HI-2 ⟩ HI	included
3	MI-2	HI-2	EI-1	excessively
2	HI-1	EI-1	EI-2 ⟩ EI	included
1	HI-2	EI-2	EI-3	

NOTES:

FI free of visible inclusions, in dark field or overhead lighting without magnification

LI lightly included, little effect on beauty, somewhat difficult to see even in dark field illumination

MI moderately included, visible marks or zoning is of minor influence on beauty of the stone in overhead light

HI heavily included, the marks tend to draw attention from the beauty of the stone in overhead light

EI excessively included, disturbing inclusions detract from the beauty of the stone.
(The author has been told that, excepting that FI was called "eye clean", this clarity grading nomenclature is similar to that used at Astro Gems in the early 1970's as introduced by Howard Rubin.)

Make

As with diamonds, a simple general description of make, such as fine, good, medium, fair, or poor provides more useful advice to the non-expert than details of proportion, symmetry, and finish. In suitable cases the quality of cutting also includes orientation to minimise, maximize, or optimize optical phenomena, colour zoning, pleochroism, and\or inclusions, and may also include artistry of design and excellence of execution in specially cut, sculpted, or carved stones.

Bear in mind that make grading of coloured gemstones differs significantly from make grading of diamonds. For coloured stones the proportion requirements will vary depending upon the colour. Tourmaline, for example, may require pavilion angles similar to those in diamond across the width of the stone but need pavilion angles on the ends that are extremely steep to reduce visibility of the black colour in the optic axis direction. A large window (an apparent opening through the centre of the stone through which one sees behind because of a shallow pavilion angle) would seriously lower the make grade of a pale or light coloured stone, while it could actually improve the appearance of a very dark coloured stone.

> **Make grade**: (noun) a designation indicating the quality of workmanship in the cut including shape, proportions, orientation, symmetry, polish, and finish details such as sharpness of facet edges, and "pointing-up" of facets.

As a quick-reference guide the following grades are suggested as a starting point for faceted stones with colours of very pale to medium tones.

10	extra fine	full brilliance, no symmetry or finish faults	
9	fine	to 10% window	
8	very good	to 20% window	Better make grades must have only minor symmetry or finish faults.
7	good	to 30% window	
6	medium-good	to 40% window	
5	medium	to 50% window	Other symmetry or finish faults will further reduce the make grade according to their severity.
4	medium-fair	to 60% window	
3	fair	to 70% window	
2	poor	to 80% window	
1	very poor	to 90% window	

Bear in mind that judgement as to make grademust consider the full properties of the material, and all of the phenomena that are, or could be, exhibited in the most carefully and knowledgeably fashioned possibility for each case.

Overall quality grade

Once the stone has been graded for colour, clarity and make, an overall quality grade must be arrived at to help establish the appropriate value. This is also a subjective judgement.

starting COLOUR grade	CLARITY / MAKE — influence toward overall quality grade			
	1 to 4	4 to 6	6 to 8	8 to 10
Commercial 1 to 4	-1.5 / -0.5	0 / 0	0 / 0	+0.25 / +0.25
Good 4 to 6	-2 / -1	-0.25 / 0	0 / 0	+0.25 / +0.25
Fine 6 to 8	-2.5 / -1.25	-0.5 / -0.25	0 / 0	+0.5 / +0.5
Extra fine 8 to 10	-3 / -1.5	-1 / -0.5	0 / 0	+0.5 / +0.5

First find the starting colour grade. To the right of the colour grade is a series of four sets of numbers in columns, each set having a number above the dashed line and one below the dashed line. The number above the line is for the influence of the clarity grade toward the final grade, the number below the line shows the influence of the make grade toward the final overall quality grade.

For example, given a type II stone graded as colour 8.5 (extra fine), clarity 7 (LI-2), and make 5 (medium) find the starting colour grade (8-10) in the leftmost column and then look at only that line of the chart, ignoring all other influence indicators.

CLARITY / MAKE influence toward overall quality grade			
starting COLOUR grade	1 to 4	4 to 6	6 to 8	8 to 10
Extra fine 8 to 10	-3	-1	**0**	+0.5
	-1.5	**-0.5**	0	+0.5

For colour 8.5, clarity 7, and make 5 the influence of clarity (0) is seen above the line in the 6 to 8 column and the influence of make (-0.5) is seen below the line in the 4 to 6 column. The final grade would be 8.5 - 0 - 0.5 = 8 (top of Fine).

Similarly, for a stone of colour grade 5 with clarity 3 and make 9 find the starting colour grade (4-6) in the leftmost column and look at only that line of the chart, ignoring all other influence indicators.

CLARITY / MAKE influence toward overall quality grade			
starting COLOUR grade	1 to 4	4 to 6	6 to 8	8 to 10
Good 4 to 6	**-2**	-0.25	0	+0.25
	-1	0	0	**+0.25**

This stone would have an overall quality grade of 3.25 according to this chart because of the clarity grade decrease of 2.0 and the make grade increase of 0.25, so although the colour and make are both good the clarity reduces the overall quality grade to commercial.

Remember that this system, or any other, is merely a guide to assist in arriving at an opinion. Once the procedure gives a final grade, consider that overall grade carefully and decide what adjustments to make (if any) for the grade to seem more reasonable. It would be absolutely correct to reduce or increase that final grade simply because the adjusted grade felt more realistic, and the only justification required is the opinion that the otherwise uncalled for adjustment seemed right.

Finally, there are gemstones that show optical phenomena. With phenomenal stones, in addition to describing all the relevant aspects of any phenomena, the quality of the phenomena must be included in the consideration of overall quality grading. Group colour and phenomena together so that the starting colour grade becomes an overall colour/phenomena grade before adding or deducting for clarity and make according to the above chart.

Grading pearls

For an outline of the necessary components for a complete description of an item of jewellery with pearls or cultured pearls, see the pearl work sheet in the appendix. Although the work-sheet presumes strung pearls, it can also be used for grading full-drilled pearls mounted on wire, for half-drilled pearls mounted on posts, or for un-drilled pearls mounted in cages.

The components of the description which comprise the grading for cultured pearls are:
- shape,
- colour,
- overtones,
- orient,
- lustre,
- complexion,
- matching, and
- nacre thickness.

For a single cultured pearl matching is not relevant, and for genuine pearls nacre thickness is not relevant, but in both these cases the other components will apply.

In the following system the grader will judge the quality of each component on a scale of one to ten with one being the lowest marginally acceptable level for that component, and ten be the very finest example for that component. The quality numbers will be used at the conclusion of the grading to arrive at an overall quality to assist with pricing. The one component which is not judged on a one-to-ten scale is orient, which is a bonus quality not seen on all pearls.

The quality numbers are for the in-house use of the appraiser, not for inclusion as part of the description for a report, because numbers will not mean anything to the non-expert client. There are also suggested adjectives for the various grade levels. These descriptive adjectives are recommended for incorporation into the appraiser's report.

Shape

The preferred shape, called round, is a completely regular sphere. In judging most bead nucleated cultured pearls, which are expected to be round, the terms suggested, with related quality numbers following in parenthesis, are:
- round (10),
- round in most (7, 8, 9)
- slightly off round (4, 5, 6)
- off round (2, 3)
- irregular (1)
- baroque
- heavily baroque

Baroque and heavily baroque would normally be considered as a separate category from round, and not valued according to round pricing. The term irregular is suggested for what has been called "semi-baroque".

Colour

Colour: (noun) the overall background base-colour behind all the features of a pearl

The colours of pearl tend to be white to very pale pastel, although fancy colours do occur and when they do they should be described by the purity, tone and hue terminology outlined earlier for coloured gemstones.

For those that are not of fancy colour, the most useful description will separate colour from overtones, and clearly distinguish them from orient.

The romantic colour terms rosé and crème are acceptable and respectively mean a very pale tone of red hue and a very pale tone of orange-brown hue.

In distinguishing colour from overtone it may be helpful to draw an analogy between the appearance of the surface of the pearl and the appearance of the skin of a lady's face. The colour of the pearl would be analogous to the lady's general skin type, her basic skin colour. Overtones would be analogous to other colour highlights on her face, such as blusher on her cheeks or powder on her nose; localized areas with additional overlaid colour. Some examples of pearl colour would include:
- white
- crème
- rosé
- pink
- yellow
- silver
- grey
- blue
- black

and modifiers or variations of these. It helps to understand that colour-modifying adjectives are part of the description of the colour and are not what is meant by overtones. In considering a colour described as "pale very slightly brownish pink" it would be incorrect to think of brown as an overtone and pale pink as the colour. The colour is the hue name together with all of the modifiers. Overtone is another issue altogether.

Overtones

> **Overtones**: (noun) localized additional colours overlaying the base colour of a pearl in patches with indistinct edge demarcations

They often occur on cultured and genuine pearls, and should be reported and considered together with the main colour to arrive at the final colour grade.
Some typical adjectives describing overtones include:

- crème,
- rosé,

- green, and
- blue.

The description should also include some indication of the extensiveness and/or strength of the overtones when they are significantly stronger, weaker or more or less widespread than might be considered usual.

Colour grade

Once the pearls has been graded for colour and overtones, an overall colour grade considering the combination of colour and overtones must be arrived at.

Different colours are preferred in different marketplaces. In a marketplace of light-skinned Caucasians, white and pink colours are preferred. Crème coloured pearls look better on darker coloured skin. Rosé overtones are the preference for all colours of pearl except black, where green overtones are most prized. On other colours of pearl, green overtones are much less desirable; a lady would not be pleased to be described as "green around the gills" which implies a comparison to stale fish!

In a Caucasian marketplace some suggested grading for colour/overtone combinations, with related quality numbers following in parenthesis, are:
- white/rosé (10, 9)
- pink/rosé (10, 9)
- black/green (10, 9)
- black/rosé (9, 8)
- pink/none (9, 8)
- white/none (8, 7)
- light crème/rosé (8, 7)
- white/slight green (7, 6)
- crème/rosé (6, 5)
- crème/none (5, 4)
- dark crème/rosé (5, 4)
- crème/green (4, 3)
- dark crème/none (4, 3)
- dark crème/green (3, 2)
- yellow/none (2, 1)

The best setting to examine pearls for colour and overtones is in the lighting environment used to examine and colour grade other coloured gems.

Orient

> **Orient**: (noun) a somewhat illusive splash of rainbow colours that chases across the surface of the nacre as a pearl, the light, or the observer moves.

When the tiny crystals of aragonite that comprise nacre happen to be small enough, and of relatively uniform size and distribution, we see the beautiful phenomenon called orient. It is not seen on every pearl because the microscopic crystals of calcium carbonate of which nacre is comprised may vary in thickness, size, and distribution pattern from one specimen to another. The concept of the thickness of the crystals should not be confused with either nacre thickness or the thickness of individual nacre layers. One might compare a cross section of the nacre on a cultured pearl with the side view of a brick building. The height of the building would compare to the full thickness of the nacre, the depth of each floor of the building would compare to the thickness of each layer of nacre, the thickness of each brick of the building would compare to the thickness of the individual crystals.

Orient was previously explained as an interference phenomenon caused by thickness of individual crystals. It was suggested that only crystals that happen to be of the appropriate thickness to cause thin-film interference would yield the iridescence. Investigations that are more recent[21] suggest that orient is a diffraction phenomenon with the colours generated depending upon the size, pattern and distribution of aragonite "tiles" across the surface. In this case the pattern generating the diffraction is statistical, not fixedly structural like a crystal lattice. The brightness of the colour phenomenon depends on the relative uniformity of the two-dimensional surface microstructure, and thus its effectiveness as a two-dimensional diffraction lattice.

---

21 Y.Liu et al, Journal of Gemmology, January 2002, Volume 28 No. 1, *Iridescence of a shell of the abalone.*

When orient is present it significantly adds to the appearance of any pearl, but it is not seen on all pearls and a necklace of cultured pearls can be of fine quality even though it does not show orient.

Orient is more often seen on irregular shapes and on uneven surfaces, but improves the quality of any pearl on which it appears. There is no orient "grade" because not all pearls are expected to show the phenomenon. Instead a bonus is added to the overall grade of pearls that do show orient according to how strong the orient is. The bonus added should be a percentage (usually no more than 50%) of the difference between the otherwise total quality-grade of the pearls and the theoretical perfect ten. For example, a cultured pearl necklace which scores six out of ten on the basis of all of its other qualities could have a bonus added for orient of up to two points, which is 50% of the difference between six and ten.

If no orient is seen, then the issue is not mentioned. This is because the absence of orient does not negate the other attractive properties of the pearls. To describe a cultured pearl necklace as having no orient could be misinterpreted to mean of very poor lustre by a non-expert. Lustre is an entirely separate issue, which deserves consideration without distraction. The approach taken is that orient adds to the quality, not that lack of orient detracts. This is more than just positive thinking, like saying a glass is half full instead of half empty. It is basic logic. Logically, a report should be about what is there, and the absence of an attribute is only reported if that attribute is normally required.

Adjectives describing various levels of orient, with suggested related quality percentage bonuses following in parenthesis are:
- perceptible (+ to 10%)
- noticeable (+ to 20%)
- significant (+ to 30%)
- strong (+ to 40%)
- very strong (+ to 50%)

The best place to examine pearls for orient may not be the lighting environment used to examine and colour grade other coloured gems. Incandescent **point-source** lighting will allow orient to be most easily seen.

> **Lustre**: (noun) the brightness and appearance of the light that is reflected from a surface.

Simple specular reflection from surface or near-surface layers is what gives lustre. The condition of the surface will influence the proportion of incident light that is reflected. The greater the quantity of incident light reflected from the surface (and sub-surface layers), the more lustrous we perceive that surface to be. An irregular surface with many microscopic pits and bumps will not reflect very much light and so will show a very dull lustre. A very smooth surface will reflect more light and have a much brighter lustre. The degree of transparency of the nacre, the thickness of the individual crystals in the nacre, and the regularity, size, and pattern of distribution of individual aragonite crystals over the surface, can modify the appearance of the reflected light.

The easiest way to judge the lustre of pearls is to look at the surface smoothness that produces the lustre. The smoother a surface, the clearer will be any reflected image from it. By shining a light on the surface of the pearls one can examine the sharpness of the reflected image of that light and match the lustre of the pearls being graded against the lustre of the pearl grading masters.

The best place to examine pearls for lustre may not be the lighting environment used to examine and colour grade other coloured gems, and will certainly not be the light source that is best to use in looking for orient. The reflection of an incandescent point-source light will be a bright point of light, and it may be difficult to judge the sharpness of a point. The reflected image of fluorescent desk lamp with a long straight bulb will look like a bright line, and it will be found that it is much easier to judge the sharpness of a line than the sharpness of a point.

Compare the sharpness of the linear image of a fluorescent tube-light on the pearls being graded against the similar image on the pearl grading masters to establish the lustre grade. Suggested names of lustre grades, with related quality numbers following in parenthesis, are:

- dull (1, 2)
- low (3, 4)
- medium (5, 6)
- bright (7, 8)
- very bright (9, 10)

Complexion

> **Complexion**: (noun) The condition and appearance of the surface of pearls with respect to the extent of surface and sub-surface irregularities such as dimples, pimples, wrinkles, or distracting dark spots.

Suggested adjectives describing complexion grades, with related quality numbers following in parenthesis, are:
- spotless (10)
- very lightly spotted (9, 8)
- lightly spotted (7, 6, 5)
- spotted (4, 3)
- heavily spotted (2)
- very heavily spotted (1)

Complexion is a completely separate issue from lustre, overtones, or orient, which are also intimately connected with surface properties. It is somewhat similar to *clarity* in a transparent stone. This similarity is based on the idea that the fewer, smaller, and less obvious the features considered, the better the quality.

Matching

> **Matching**: (noun) the extent to which individual characteristics and overall appearance of each pearl is the same as every other pearl in a group.

Wide variations in the pearls in one necklace add a distraction from the beauty of the pearls. An observer may notice the variations to such an extent that a significant portion of the beauty is overlooked. The more closely the pearls in an item match one another, the more an observer notices the beauty of the pearls rather than the differences between them.

Suggested adjectives to describe matching grades, with related quality numbers following in parenthesis, are:
- poor (1, 2)
- fair (3, 4)
- good (5, 6)
- very good (7, 8)
- excellent (9, 10)

Nacre thickness

In the formative years of the cultured pearl industry, nacre thickness was so great that discriminating cultured pearls from the genuine article was quite problematic. Indeed, it may fairly be said that the advent of the cultured pearl was probably the greatest single impetus to the development of classes in gemmology, gemmological organisations, and gem trade laboratories.

In 1907 two Japanese experimenters (first Mise then Nishikawa) separately applied for patents on cultured cyst pearl production. In 1908 the Gemmological Association was formed as a committee of the National Association of Goldsmiths to offer courses in gem identification in Great Britain, and students from these and subsequent courses in London founded other organisations around the world. In 1912 G. F. Herbert Smith's book Gemstones became the first scientific gemmology text. In the early 1920's commercially grown cultured pearls began appearing on the market and in 1925 the London Chamber of Commerce Pearl and Gem Testing Laboratory (under the direction of Basil Anderson) was created to answer the needs of the jewellery industry in diagnosing cultured pearls (and other gems).

With the general acceptance of cultured pearls and growth of the cultured pearl market, demand outstripped supply. Producers soon succumbed to temptation and shortened the culturing time to increase production, sales, and profits. Cultured pearls were being produced with thinner and thinner layers of nacre as the growing times reduced below three years and later to below one year for many cultured pearls. When some pearls were being harvested after only a few months, the Japanese industry recognised the danger the "quick-dip" product represented to their image. They influenced their government to legislate minimum standards, and cultured pearls which are inspected and do not meet the minimum standard are destroyed.

Identification of most cultured pearls has become less problematic with thinner nacre coatings on the mother-of-pearl beads, but it means that nacre thickness itself has become a quality issue for cultured pearls.

Suggested adjectives to describe nacre thickness and the thickness range for each step, with related quality numbers following in parenthesis, are:
- below standard, <0.15 mm (1)
- standard, 0.15<0.30 mm (2, 3)
- standard+ (or medium), 0.30<0.45 mm (4, 5, 6)
- medium-thick, 0.45<0.60 mm (7, 8)
- thick, 0.60<0.90 mm (9, 10)
- very thick >0.90 mm (10+)

Very thick nacre is unusual in modern cultured pearls so a bonus, with a quality number larger than 10 is reasonable even though the nominal range of the quality scale is from one to ten.

Overall quality

To arrive at an overall quality each quality component is first weighted. Then the weighted components are added together for a total quality grade, again on a scale of from one to ten. If the pearls exhibit orient, a bonus is then added to the total to give the final quality grade.
Suggested weightings for each of the one-to-ten quality components are:
- **shape** @ 15% (i.e. multiply the shape quality number by 0.15)
- **colour/overtone** @ 10% (i.e. multiply the quality number by 0.10)
- **lustre** @ 25% (i.e. multiply the lustre quality number by 0.25)
- **complexion** @ 20% (i.e. multiply the complexion quality by 0.20)
- **matching** @ 05% (i.e. multiply the matching quality by 0.05)
- **nacre** @ 25% (i.e. multiply the nacre quality number by 0.25)
to give a 100% total of between one and ten for the general quality grade.

When the pearls show orient, the numerical difference between the general total quality grade and ten is multiplied by the **orient bonus** percent to set the bonus number (to one decimal place, ignoring the second decimal place unless it is a 9) to be added to the general total quality grade for the final total quality grade.

An example may clarify. The following description is accompanied by the quality grade numbers, and there follows the calculations to arrive at the general total quality grade supplemented by the calculation for orient bonus and its addition to make the final total quality grade:

➤ round-in-most (8), light crème colour with rosé overtones (7), noticeable orient (20%), medium lustre (5), lightly spotted (6), good matching (6), and standard+ nacre (6)...

(8 x 0.15)+(7 x 0.10)+(5 x 0.25)+(6 x 0.20)+(6 x 0.05)+(6 x 0.25)

= 6.15

orient bonus @ 20% >> (10 - 6.15) x 0.20

= 0.77

Final total quality grade 6.15 + 0.70 = 6.85

The calculations set them near the centre of the "fine" range of quality when 1 to 4 is commercial, 4 to 6 is good, 6 to 8 is fine and 8 to 10 is extra fine.

Appraisal content

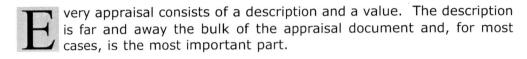

Every appraisal consists of a description and a value. The description is far and away the bulk of the appraisal document and, for most cases, is the most important part.

Description details

The content of the description can be broadly divided into two general categories of information.

Firstly there is factual data, hard facts that are measurable and incontrovertible. These can be ascertained using measuring devices when there is no component of interpretation, no element of personal judgement involved. Factual data are the recorded measurements of physical (including optical) properties.

Factual data normally specified in a report would include weights and dimensions. Other factual data, such as specific gravity, refractive index, birefringence, optical character, optic sign, luminescent response, spectrophotometric analysis, and so on, would be included in the report in only very particular cases. In most cases such factual data would be analysed by the appraiser to arrive at conclusions and the conclusions of that analysis reported.

The result of analysis, or any conclusion which incorporates an element of judgement, is an opinion — which is the second category of information. Limiting factors for factual data will be the calibration and precision of instruments or devices used. Limiting factors for opinions will include knowledge, insights, skills, and judgements. The equipment used to measure data should be of the greatest accuracy and precision applicable, and opinions should be arrived at with the greatest possible conscientious care and integrity.

On an appraisal it must be perfectly clear whether each item of information is a factual datum or an opinion. The reported weight of a gemstone, for example, could be either. If the carat weight was calculated from dimensions then it is opinion, even though the dimensions are factual data. The carat weight would be part of the factual data in an appraisal if the stone actually was weighed while un-mounted.

For diamonds; (number), identification, outline shape, style of cut, dimensions, (total) carat weight, colour grade, clarity grade and make (quality of cut). Luminescent response to ultraviolet light is optional information that can be helpful in re-identification.

The word brilliant should not be used as a noun to mean diamond. Do not say "six brilliants" but rather say "six diamonds" followed by details of style of cut, etcetera.

For coloured stones; (number), identification, shape, dimensions, style of cut, transparency, colour purity, colour tone, hue, colour distribution, optical phenomena, clarity grade, make, and (total) carat weight.

For pearls; (number), mm dimension(s), variation, shape, type, body colour, overtones, orient (if any), lustre, complexion, matching, nacre thickness, length of necklace (including clasp), length(s) of strands (excluding clasp), number in each strand, stringing method, attachment to the clasp.

See the pearl work sheet in the appendix.

Regarding type and source; if the pearls are natural, specify the basis on which this identification was made including the name of the identifying laboratory and tests performed. An identification that is tentative or assumed must be so specified!

Small (minor) stones; may be grouped and described together only if they are of similar size and qualities stating identification, style of cut, dimensions, the average or the range of colour, clarity, make and/or any other species/variety-specific qualities. Include a count of the stones and their total carat weight.

Stones of insignificant value; may be grouped and described together in more general terms, for example "...twelve faceted smoky quartz, six round, four oval and two marquise shape, 0.05 to 0.12 carat, weighing in total approximately 1.25 carats, of light colours and fair quality..."

In descriptions report only those qualities and data that were directly observed or measured (or were observed or measured under subcontract). If any part of the description is tentative or assumed, be sure to specify so in the appraisal.

It is appropriate in some cases to hypothesize changes to an item in arriving at a value, but when this is done it must be clearly stated in the appraisal. If an important stone in an article is damaged, for example, it might be specified that "the stated value is based on a hypothetical re-cut of the centre stone with an estimated yield of approximately 1.22 carats". In the case of an old European cut or old mine cut diamond the valuation may be based upon a hypothetical re-cut while at the same time specifying ... "we do not recommend that a re-cutting of the stone actually be performed," but valuation on this basis of a hypothetical re-cut should be done with due caution. Some older cut stones, particularly finer colour and clarity stones of better make for their style of cut, can only be valued as period stones. This is particularly obvious for more important (i.e. larger and better quality) stones or those that have significant provenance.

An example when a hypothetical re-cut approach to valuation would be more appropriate is an insurance appraisal of a solitaire engagement ring of modern manufacture containing an old mine cut diamond salvaged from a family heirloom that had been worn or damaged beyond repair. In this case the insured and the insurer both understand that if the ring is stolen the replacement item would be a new ring containing a modern brilliant cut diamond of comparable size and qualities, so the hypothesis of re-cut yield is both reasonable and helpful. It would be much less reasonable to appraise an antique item this way because it is usually not assumed that the antique would be replaced with a new item, rather it is assumed it would be replaced with an antique and so costing the stones as old style of cut must be assumed to cover such a replacement, or to cover the case of repair or replacement of a lost or damaged stone.

Finally, do not pad the description with irrelevant jargon or quoted data from standard references. The appraisal is supposed to be a report of professional conclusions, not plagiarized reference data. Some appraisers feel that an impressive list of equipment and materials helps justify the fee charged. In listing equipment and materials used to perform the -

appraisal **be sure** each indicated item actually was used. If the appraisal form lists all the equipment, resources and materials in the appraising laboratory, check off those actually used to perform that particular appraisal. Otherwise such lists are just obvious padding and will diminish the credibility of the rest of the report.

Valuation

Bearing in mind the valuation level, decide which valuation approach to use.

The market data comparison approach requires research in the most common marketplace in which such merchandise is sold to such persons as the hypothetical purchaser. For standard jewellery items of modern manufacture it would be appropriate to investigate asking prices of comparable items to establish the value. For important items, including those of modern manufacture, costs in actual sales will yield a more defensible opinion of value.

To use the costing approach, costs of all the components to the hypothetical vendor must be established and then any hidden taxes and an appropriate mark-up (or discount) factored in. Remember to standardize the definition of the hypothetical vendor and the mark-up schedule(s) for typical cases.

When a trademark or maker's mark indicates that there is significant provenance in the name of the designer or vendor, the application of standard mark-ups to perceived cost may not be a valid valuation approach. The famous and/or highly renowned can routinely charge significantly more!

Metal
It is a bit difficult to discuss costs without mentioning figures. Prices quoted are **$ Canadian** in Toronto. Check the local marketplace to determine appropriate current costs.

Here are some suggested formulae for calculating the value of gold (from bullion to wholesale cost to retail) on a per gram basis. The wording in block capitals indicates the valuation level.

STRATEGIES AND FORMULAE to get the *PER GRAM* VALUE
($G = $ per ounce gold fix) (K = Karat number)

RAW BULLION:	$G/31.1035 x K/24
SCRAP (small quantity):	$G/1350 x K to $G/1234 x K
SCRAP (bulk):	$G/944 x K
REFINED GOLD:	$G/31.1035 x K/24 x 1.05
ROUGH CASTING:	refined gold value + ($0.25 to $15.00)
BULK MACHINE MADE:	refined gold value x 1.25
FINISHED MACHINE MADE:	bulk machine made value + ($0.75 to $3.25)
ITALIAN MACHINE MADE:	as local + premium of up to 30%

Finished gold jewellery should be costed out at the raw gold value plus refining charges and manufacturer's mark-up on the gold (together typically up to 40%). In addition, a labour charge plus a distributor's mark-up (perhaps 30%) plus setting charges must be included. Then hidden taxes and mark-ups to retail can be applied.

Labour

For a simple one-piece item to be cast, ground and polished the labour may cost as little as $4 to $9 if hastily done or as much as $25 or more if done with care and attention to detail.

Two or three piece assemblies of cast or stamped parts have a higher labour cost of from $20 to $90 or more depending on the complexity, quality of components and quality of finish.

Additional refinements such as texturing or Florentine finish should be examined closely to see if they are hiding problems such as excessive use of solder or porosity of the metal. Such extra finishing should add to the cost by only a few dollars unless it is exceptional.

Hand-made metal-smith labour is much more expensive than production run goods. Fine work on a simple hand-made piece can start at $65 with a limit well into the thousands for a complex valuable item.

Modifications to standard designs and creation of new designs require a design labour charge in addition to the metal-smith work. This may be $50 or less if the modification is minor, or as much as $1,000 or more if it is an original design.

Eighteen Karat white gold is harder than many other gold alloys and labour charges in this and some other specialty alloys may be a little higher.

Platinum labour cost is very much higher than gold, perhaps four to ten times the labour on comparable gold items. Setting costs in platinum are typically four or five times (or more) the charges in gold. With raw platinum costing $600 an ounce, a simple cast platinum item might cost $125 per gram. A hand-finished platinum solitaire ring might cost $150 per gram. Platinum cluster rings could cost $200 per gram or more.

Mark-ups

The mark-ups one would use to arrive at retail replacement value should be on a sliding scale with low cost items having the highest mark-up. I have three mark-up schedules; one for diamonds (or very fine jewellery without diamonds), another for cultured pearls and jewellery set with coloured stones, the third for plain gold jewellery. They assume that the hypothetical vendor is a single location small volume retailer who produces or acquires stock on a single item or minimum quantity basis.

Basic jewellery such as machine made plain gold might be marked up at keystone (100% or cost times 2), reducing to 25% (cost times 1.25) for costs over $50,000.

Standard jewellery such as a cultured pearl necklace might be marked up by 130% (or cost times 2.3) reducing to 25% (cost times 1.25) for costs in excess of $50,000.

Diamond-set and other **fine** jewellery might be marked up by 150% (cost times 2.5) reducing to 25% (cost times 1.25). when cost exceeds $50,000.

In the following example mark-up schedules CTI means "the wholesale Cost with hidden Taxes Included".

Mark-ups for **fine** (e.g. diamond) jewellery
CTI x 2.5 = RETAIL
(CTI - 500) x 2 + 1250 = RETAIL
(CTI - 1000) x 1.6 + 2250 = RETAIL
(CTI - 3000) x 1.4 + 5450 = RETAIL
(CTI - 5000) x 1.3 + 8250 = RETAIL
(CTI - 10000) x 1.2 + 14750 = RETAIL
(CTI - 25000) x 1.19 + 32750 = RETAIL
for CTI over 50,000 then ... CTI x 1.25 = RETAIL

Mark-ups for **standard** (e.g. cultured pearl) jewellery

CTI x 2.3 = RETAIL
(CTI - 500) x 1.92 + 1150 = RETAIL
(CTI - 1000) x 1.66 + 2110 = RETAIL
(CTI - 3000) x 1.41 + 5430 = RETAIL
(CTI - 5000) x 1.3 + 8250 = RETAIL
(CTI - 10000) x 1.2 + 14750 = RETAIL
(CTI - 25000) x 1.19 + 32750 = RETAIL
for CTI over 50,000 then ... CTI x 1.25 = RETAIL

Mark-ups for **basic** (e.g. plain gold) jewellery

$$\text{CTI} \times 2 = \text{RETAIL}$$
$$(\text{CTI} - 500) \times 1.98 + 1000 = \text{RETAIL}$$
$$(\text{CTI} - 1000) \times 1.67 + 1990 = \text{RETAIL}$$
$$(\text{CTI} - 3000) \times 1.46 + 5330 = \text{RETAIL}$$
$$(\text{CTI} - 5000) \times 1.3 + 8250 = \text{RETAIL}$$
$$(\text{CTI} - 10000) \times 1.2 + 14750 = \text{RETAIL}$$
$$(\text{CTI} - 25000) \times 1.19 + 32750 = \text{RETAIL}$$
$$\text{for CTI over 50,000 then} \ldots \text{CTI} \times 1.25 = \text{RETAIL}$$

The mark-up schedule used should be the most appropriate for the kind of article being valued, and the appraiser should be prepared to change mark-up schedules to reflect the time, place and/or provenance. This particularly applies when a trademark or maker's mark indicates that there is significant provenance in the name of the designer or vendor. The hypothesized single location small-volume retailer could not possibly sell new merchandise with such markings, so these mark-up schedules would not apply. The famous and/or highly renowned can routinely charge significantly more than would be asked for comparable quality material and workmanship produced by anonymous craftsmen and retailed by a hypothetical typical vendor!

The preceding mark-ups differ from those used in the example offered later in the appendix because the example appraisal relates to a different time.

One could also hypothesize the vendor as an insurance replacement specialist, and establish a similar mark-up schedule for replacement/ reproduction value. This approach should satisfy the insurance industry's requirement that value for insurance be the full amount that might realistically be paid for an identical or a comparable (whichever is specifically required) item sold in an appropriate market (as defined by the hypothetical purchaser and vendor) for the personal use of the ultimate or final customer.

Worksheets and documentation

Design a work sheet that feels comfortable and logical. It may not work just to adopt someone else's standard layout but considering someone else's format may save hours of trial-and-error form drafting. In organizing the work sheet it may be helpful to keep calculations for each cost in one line and keep the extended totals in one column. This allows quick easy checking of each step of the costing process, including the arithmetic. All relevant information should be on the work sheet and particularly make sure to record the source or rationale for pricing anything other than the most ordinary goods.

Maintain a permanent record of all work sheets produced as well as of appraisals. If performing appraisals while employed, the related files belong to the employer. If performing appraisals under subcontract for a store, the files are the appraiser's property even though the retail consumer would be the store's client.

When a request is received for information about an appraisal that was previously done it would be good practice to append a note to that file recording all details. It may later be desirable to know the identity of the person, the nature of the request, the date, and specifics of the response. Seek advice if there are doubts about how (or if) a request should be responded to. Take every precaution to safeguard the original records. Do not give anyone the originals unless required to by law and then ensure that copies are retained.

The appraisal document

Some appraisal commissions may require particular reporting formats (see p46) but with most appraisals, such as those for insurance, one can format the required information onto a single page standardized form.

The appraisal should include:
o   Name of the company responsible for the appraisal
o   Name of the person, company, institution or government department that commissioned the appraisal
o   Date the appraisal was performed
o   Valuation date if different from the date of appraisal

- Base price of the metal if the costing approach was used. In an appraisal for insurance an incremental base price of the metal, such as gold at the nearest $25 increment, is quite justifiable. Some more formal appraisals may require that the spot price of the metal on the valuation date be used
- Full detailed description of the article(s) including: type of item, design, composition, qualities, quantification, condition and authenticity; with an individual detailed description of each major gemstone and appropriate descriptions of the minor stones grouped into like value categories as established by variety, size, and qualities
- Quality marks, hallmarks, trade marks, or other markings
- Accurate gross weight of each item
- Value of each item or set of like articles. Where a value is given for a set of like articles the value is for the whole set and there is no implication of the individual or proportionate values of articles within the set unless a single item part-set value is separately specifically stated
- Valuation basis if other than retail replacement for insurance
- Declaration of costing presumptions; for example, the bracketed colour grade which was assumed in costing an important mounted diamond; or, that the appraisal presumes any replacement will be by the client's choice of retailer if retail replacement value is not elsewhere defined
- Limiting appraisal conditions, if any. If the appraisal was performed outside of the laboratory, without the use of the full range of equipment, under pressure of time limits, under the continuous observation of the client, or under any other limiting constraints such as poor lighting, sealed packaging, or confined space, these conditions should be specified on the appraisal document
- The typed name and qualifications of the appraiser
- A true signature of the appraiser or a representative of the firm responsible for the appraisal (The signature on an appraisal is to confirm or bear witness that the named appraiser performed the examination and analysis of the item(s) appraised. In addition the signature indicates the company's (&/or the appraiser's) acceptance of responsibility for the content of the appraisal.)
- In cases of particular or unusual design an optional photograph may be helpful in re-identification or duplication, but use of a photograph

should never mean a reduction in detail of the description. To offer a less than complete description and say "see photograph for details" is entirely inappropriate and most unprofessional. The significance of a photograph of an item appraised for insurance will depend upon the item itself and the purpose and applications of the appraisal. For a simple one-piece cast ring with some design features in its shape, a photograph may be considered necessary when duplication value is reported. If retail replacement value or replacement / reproduction value is reported, a photograph may actually be misleading in that the client might consider the design details to be of too great a significance if she does not understand that a **comparable** replacement does **not** mean a **duplicate**.

Other format considerations

Use a pre-printed appraisal form that includes appropriate general information and disclosures including:

- A logo, address and telephone number
- A statement of responsibilities regarding the content of and the appropriate uses for the appraisal
- A policy statement regarding reporting of metal qualities
- An explanation and policy statement about limitations inherent in grading, measuring and estimating weights of mounted stones
- A policy statement regarding the reporting of ordinary wear common to the type of article appraised
- A policy statement regarding retail sales tax and the value.
- The reverse of the printed appraisal form and/or the cover sheet may list information about terminology, grading systems, general explanations and helpful suggestions such as care, cleaning and storage of jewellery and recommended frequency of re-appraisal. By putting such general information here rather than on the face of the appraisal it will provide more space on the appraisal form for specific information and data
- Position descriptions on the form to eliminate the possibility of someone inserting description and value of other items
- When there is more than one item on an appraisal enumerate each and, following the description and value of the last item, indicate the number of items and the total of their values

- Cover or emboss the signature and each valuation amount with a tamper-proof seal
- When an appraisal extends to more than one page, always type the page number and total number of pages on each and every page (e.g. "page 2 of 5") and on the last page following the description and value of the last article indicate the number of items appraised and their total value. Seal the page numbers and total value in the same way each item value and the signature are sealed
- When a valuation is at other than retail replacement value indicate the purview (scope of appropriate applications) by specifying the assigned use.

Special report of tangible property

The format outlined below is much more formal than the typical valuation for insurance. See the example in the appendix p183.

1. Letter of transmittal
This is the covering letter for the report and includes a brief summary of the report and its conclusions. It should refer to the report and each of the exhibits at the end of the report.

2. Title page
This may include date of report, title of report, name of the author and his company with address and telephone number, and may include the name and address of the person, department, or organisation that commissioned the report, but the title of the report should be most prominent.

3. Table of contents
List all of the following items that are included.

4. Purpose of the appraisal
A statement of the intended purpose for the appraisal, why it was commissioned (in general terms), the purview (scope of appropriate applications), definition(s) of the valuation level(s) used, and the effective valuation dates.

5. Limiting conditions (if any)
Be sure to record any and all limiting conditions in your notes. If you are later required to give testimony at litigation, it could be difficult to rationalize a declaration of limiting conditions not recorded at the time.

6. Photograph(s) (if appropriate)

If the number of photographs is large they should be included as an appendix. Significance of photographs will depend upon the items as well as the purpose and applications of the appraisal. For a simple cast ring, a photograph may be necessary to show design details when reporting duplication value. Retail replacement value or replacement / reproduction value, however, presumes replacement with comparable. Photographs may actually be misleading in that the client might consider design details to be of too great significance if she does not understand that comparable does **not** mean a duplicate.

7. Property description

This should be a full description of the article(s) being appraised. If there are many items or if the description is lengthy an appendix should be used. When an appendix is used the description in the body of the report may be more general [e.g. twelve (12) articles of gem set jewellery described in detail in appendix "A" attached].

8. Appraisal process and analysis

Explain the procedures used including date(s) of inspection, details of analysis, references used, consultations, valuation level, information sources for value, and finally conclusion(s) reached with the basis for the conclusion.

This section of the report should end with a clear statement of the opinion of the value of the property as of the effective valuation date.

9. Qualifications of the appraiser

Education: may include general education but must include specific education history relevant to the claimed area of expertise in gems and jewellery appraising, including designations earned by examination.

Affiliations: memberships, designations held by appointment, honours conferred by industry organisations.

Experience: including employment, business contracts, significant case experience, court experience, etcetera.

10. Appraiser's certificate

A dated and signed statement that the appraiser:

- o   Has no interest in the property evaluated in the report
- o   Has personally inspected every article described

and that ...

- o   Neither the commission to perform the examination and produce the report nor the fee for professional services is contingent upon the estimate of value
- o   Any other statement of significance such as knowledge of and/or relationship to any of the principals concerned.

11. Appendices

These should include any and all significant documents and should be labelled with capital letters (A, B, C etc.) or Roman numerals.

Sources of information

General appraising

The Practical Guide to Jewelry Appraising, C. Altobelli, Edited by R. S. Joseph, American Gem Society, 2000

Handbook of Jewelry and Gemstone Appraising, C. Altobelli and C. Preston, American Gem Society, 1986

Gems and Jewelry Appraising, (Techniques of Professional Practice), A.M. Miller, Van Nostrand Reinhold, 1988

Illustrated Guide to Jewelry Appraising, (Antique, Period & Modern), A.M. Miller, Van Nostrand Reinhold, 1990

The Guide Reference Manual, Gemworld International Inc., 630 Dundee Rd., Suite 235, Northbrook IL 60062 USA

Registered Valuer's Guidelines, Valuations Committee of the National Association of Goldsmiths, 78a Luke St., London EC2A 4PY

Pricing

The most important source of information on pricing should be the appraiser's own knowledge and carefully recorded log of pricing information. Of course decisions on prices will always be recorded on the work sheets, but it will be extremely helpful to append that information into a pricing log.

Always bear in mind that no one price source is complete; therefore consider what other pricing information is available. **Contacts in the industry** are far and away the most valuable asset in appraising. No matter one's level of experience and knowledge, one must regularly seek advice and assistance in pricing. Important, rare, and unusual items as well as special designer pieces automatically require extra research in valuing them.

Cultivate a circle of contacts who can be asked about prices in specific categories such as: inexpensive gemstones, diamonds, pearls, specific gem species, rare and collector gems, exceptionally fine or important stones, collectibles, antiques, watches, silver/ gold/ or platinum metal work.

There can be very significant differences in the opinion of value between competent appraisals even when there is little difference in judgements of the relevant qualities. When competent appraisals disagree even slightly in the judgements of the relevant qualities, valuations can differ dramatically.

When appraised values agree within 40% of the lower value this should be considered essential agreement. Depending on the items, a variance of as much as 65% to 80% of the lower value could be considered as within reason and quite defensible. Narrower tolerances would only be appropriate for commercially available diamonds of unexceptional size, which were accurately graded while loose. Wider tolerances would be more appropriate for an item that was unique.

Nearly identical valuations between independent appraisals are an unusual coincidence unless the appraisers either consult with each other or use identical pricing strategies and both consult with exactly the same pricing experts.

Books

The Price Guide To Jewellery, 3000 BC to 1950 AD, (1976, prices revised 1982), M. Poynder, Baron Publishing, Antique Collectors' Club, 5 Church Street, Woodbridge, Suffolk, England

Sotheby's International Price Guide, The Vendome Press, Methuen Publications

Jade For You, J. Y. Ng and E. Root, Jade N Gem Corp. of America 610 S. Broadway Suite 615, Los Angeles, CA 90014, USA

A Field Guide to Australian Opals, (1984), Barrie O'Leary. Gemcraft ltd., 291-293 Wattletree Rd., E. Malvern, Vic., 3145, Australia

Opal Identification and Value[22], (1992), Paul B. Downing, Majestic Press, P. O. Box 14229, Tallahassee, FL 32317-4229, USA

Subscriptions & catalogues

Gemworld Price Guide, Gemworld International Inc., 630 Dundee Road, Suite 235, Northbrook, IL 60062, USA

Palmieri's **GAA Market Monitor**, Gemological Appraisal Association Inc., 650 Washington Road, Pittsburgh, PA 15228, USA

DiamExpress (the official gemstone price guide of the NAG Registered Valuers), Amalgamated Diamond Brokers, High Street, Whitchurch, Aylesbury, Bucks, HP22 4JH, England

Rapaport Diamond Report, 15 West 47th Street, New York, NY 10036, USA

---

[22] A very useful opal grading and pricing system. Paul also offers sets of opal grading masters for comparing brightness levels of play of colour. Gemmologists will find that he makes the error of referring to play of colour as "fire" (fire is the rainbow colours caused by dispersion seen in diamond and other faceted stones), but this minor error does not diminish the usefulness of the grading system, which is the grading used in the opal section of the *Gemworld Price Guide*.

Sotheby's, auction catalogues and sale results, 9 Hazelton Avenue, Toronto, ON, M5R 2E1, Canada

Dupuis', auction catalogues and sales results, #687-1755 Robson Street, Vancouver, B.C. V6G 3B7, Canada

The NCJV Valuer, National Council of Jewellery Valuers, P.O. Box Q605, QVB Post Shop, Sydney NSW 1230, Australia

General research

An appraiser needs an extensive research library of gemmology and jewellery books for researching identity and authenticity.

It is unrealistic to try to comprehensively list every available book suitable for incorporating into the appraiser's library. The following are a few books that may be found useful.

Gemmology & gem identification

Gems, Their Source, Description and Identification, (5th Ed. 1994), Robert Webster, Butterworths

Handbook of Gem Identification, (12th Ed. 1987), Richard T. Liddicoat Jr., GIA

Gemstones, (1988), Michael O'Donoghue, Chapman and Hall

Photoatlas of Inclusions in Gemstones, (1986), E. J. Gubelin and J. I. Koivula, ABC Edition

Color Encyclopedia of Gems, (2nd Ed. 1987), Joel E. Arem, Van Nostrand Reinhold

Determinative Gemology, W. William Hanneman, Hanneman Gemological Instruments, PO Box 942 Poulsbo, WA 98370, USA

Gemstone Enhancement, (2nd Ed. 1994), Kurt Nassau, Butterworth

Encyclopedia of Minerals, (2nd Ed. 1990), Willard L. Roberts, Thomas J. Campbell and George R. Rapp Jr., Van Nostrand Reinhold

Gemmological publications

The Journal of Gemmology, 27 Greville St., London EC1N 8SU, England

The Canadian Gemmologist, 1767 Avenue Road, Toronto ON, M5M 3Y8, Canada

The Australian Gemmologist, Box 477, Albany Creek Q.4035, Australia

Gems & Gemology, 5345 Armada Drive, Carlsbad CA 92008, USA

Metals

Poinçons d'Or et de Platine, Tardy

International Hallmarks on Silver, Tardy

Brand Name and Trademark Guide, Jewellers' Circular-Keystone

Trade Mark Index, Canadian Jeweller Magazine

Watches

The Complete Guide to American Pocket Watches, Cooksey Shugart and Tom Engle, Overstreet Publications

Vintage American & European Wrist Watch Price Guide, Sherry Ehrhardt & Peter Planes, Heart of America Press

Coins

The Standard Catalogue of World Coins, Chester L. Krause and Clifford Mishler, Krause Publications

Specialty subjects

Acquire a wide selection of specialty books on antique and period jewellery, famous jewellers and designers, individual gem species and so on, as well as subscribe to trade magazines such as Jewellery World and Jewellers' Circular Keystone.

Delivery to the client

Presentation

The purpose of an appraisal is to provide the customer with information. When the customer receives the appraisal is the appropriate time to answer any questions and counsel the customer concerning the proper application (s) of the appraisal. Make sure he understands the uses appropriate for the kind of appraisal as well as the meaning of the content. The explanations and advice will be appreciated and will help justify the appraisal fee.

If the appraisal was produced for a store at a wholesale fee less than retail, the store should be responsible for the interaction with and explanations to their customer.

Remuneration

Not that long ago the standard method of charging for appraisal work was based entirely on a percentage of the total value of all items appraised. This produced a tendency toward extremely optimistic values that were sometimes beyond all reasonable bounds producing inflated appraisal fees and over insured clients. When the fee is based on the value of the article the appraiser necessarily has a vested interest in that value, which may arguably compromise the impartiality of the opinion. Note that under item 10 of the Special Appraisal Report (**appraiser's certificate,** p.131, 189) the fee for professional service **should not** be contingent upon the estimate of value.
It is more appropriate to charge fees based on the time and effort necessary to produce the appraisal, bearing in mind that the charges are for **expertise, not just labours.** This can be accomplished in different ways:

- Charge a straight hourly rate, with an estimate to the customer at take-in of the length of time expected to be necessary
- Set a per item rate which might be a sliding scale according to the complexity of each item and the sizes and types of stones it contains
- Similarly set up a schedule with a basic item fee with additional surcharges for items of particular types of jewellery, number of different kinds of gemstones, incremental total diamond weight, incremental total weights of coloured stones, number of charms, etcetera
- A plausible hybrid approach is to have a fee schedule with the sliding scale charge for each item related to broad ranges of appraised value. This differs from a fee set as a straight percentage of value, and may be justified as an acceptable structure provided that the lowest range of values (i.e. for items carrying the lowest fee) is broad enough to include the majority of jewellery articles currently being retailed
- It might even be possible to set out a fee schedule based upon the tests performed and equipment and materials used to perform the appraisal work (although this would be a cumbersome fee structure to use).

It is usual to have a minimum retail appraisal fee.

In addition to private practice one may also do appraisal work for manufacturers or retailers under arrangements only limited by the imaginations of the principals concerned. A possibility would be for a retailer to provide rent-free space for on-site appraisals to service his customers while the appraiser provides the equipment and keeps all proceeds generated (the store increases traffic and clientele by providing on-the-spot service). Another on-site possibility would be as an employee of the retailer on a salary, commission or combination basis (influenced by who provides the equipment, materials, secure storage, insurance, advertising, etc.) with the retailer handling all proceeds.

When doing subcontract appraisal work for a store there should be a clear understanding between the store and the appraiser. The appraiser should not undercut the retail appraisal fee charged by the store. The store should not expect the appraiser to be involved in dealing with or explaining things to the retail client.

Liability and responsibility[23]

Understanding the obligations

A professional jewellery appraiser has responsibilities on a number of levels to a number of different people including the client, third parties, the appraising profession, the jewellery industry, the legal community and the general public.

First of all there are responsibilities for the handling and safe keeping when accepting custody of the goods. As explained previously, when accepting custody of someone else's property, there is an obligation to care for that property at least as carefully as a reasonable person would in the same situation. The level of care with which other goods are handled may be almost irrelevant. Everyone is entitled to handle his own goods negligently (and suffer any results). The central point in any dispute is **what would be reasonable** for the prudent person in a like situation. If negligence causes damage, there is liability for whatever wrong negligence has caused, subject to the limits of liability agreed upon by the client at take in.

The extent of liability regarding loss or damage is governed by a number of considerations. First, there is the mutual understanding of the parties concerned. When the understanding of the principals is not in accord, then the second consideration would be usual or customary practices. The content of any contract (verbal or recorded) would take precedence over the first two considerations. In almost all situations, a contract cannot contravene any legislation that might apply. Finally, interpretation of the whole or any part of a contract, or interpretation of liability under usual or customary practices, could be subject to litigation.

In the final analysis a court may have to decide whether a party has liability and, if so, the proper extent of the damage suffered by the other. If there is a written legal contract with wording that a reasonable person would not misunderstand, it is very unlikely that any dispute will go as far as being presented to a judge or to a judge and jury for determination.

---

[23] NOTE: This information is not legal opinion or legal advice. Reading, viewing, or receiving it does not create or constitute an attorney-client relationship.

A clause in the take in contract can limit liability. If it is to withstand legal challenges, the disclaimer must define a limit of liability that is reasonable. An unreasonable disclaimer such as *"Our liability in the event of loss or damage is limited to $100"* could be determined to be invalid, which is as bad as having no disclaimer at all. A more realistic disclaimer might read: *"Our liability in the event of loss or damage is limited to the declared value or the cost of repair or replacement, whichever is less".*

It is important to have a meaningful liability-limiting clause. Without such a clause liability can extend to consequential and/or punitive damages (e.g. for sentimental value) if negligence is determined. Consult with a lawyer about appropriate wording as well as the positioning and relative prominence of the clause in the contract. Small print in an inconspicuous place may make the clause ineffective!

The well known expression "a verbal contract isn't worth the paper it's written on" has misled many people into thinking a verbal contract is not valid and would not be found binding. This is quite wrong. The disadvantage of an oral contract is that it is not recorded and, accordingly, it is much more difficult for parties to prove that it exists and that there was a shared understanding as to its terms. It is just as binding, however, as a written contract. Whenever accepting custody of goods from someone in circumstances where there is no standard take in contract for them to read, tell them that the basis for accepting custody must be with liability limited to the cost of repair or replacement only. If they mention sentimental value be particularly careful to disclaim any responsibility for sentimental value or consequential damage.

Responsibility extends well beyond the handling and safe keeping of the goods. In addition there is responsibility regarding the work that was undertaken. The appraiser was commissioned to provide an expert opinion and must therefore exert due diligence and integrity and provide an opinion that will fulfil the legitimate needs of the consumer to the best of his ability.

First and foremost the appraisal must actually be the appraiser's expert opinion. It must not simply accommodate someone else's expectations or desires. If someone seeks an appraisal with particular wording or value, an accommodating appraisal would be fraudulent and could easily be judged to be criminal. Similarly, if an employed appraiser is instructed to issue an appraisal with specific wording or content, the appraiser and his boss could both be committing a criminal act unless the appraiser has duly considered, understands, and agrees with the grounds for and content of that appraisal. In the second instance, if the boss felt he had reasonable grounds for the appraisal content he dictated, he could legitimately require an employee to prepare a document with the wording he wants even if the subordinate disputes the content. His role as the boss gives him authority to issue instructions if those instructions are legal. For it to be a legitimate appraisal, however, the name of the person officially issuing the document should be his, not the instructed employee (although on his instructions the employee may sign the document on his behalf). The opinion in an appraisal must be that of the named appraiser.

The official record of the expert opinion, the appraisal, must provide useful information that is understandable. Be careful in employment of any scientific terminology or trade jargon. The consumer should be able to understand and rely on the report to make informed decisions and one cannot presume a consumer will understand special terminology. The appraisal should present the information clearly and concisely with content and format that precludes, as much as possible, any person misrepresenting the expert opinion to a third party.

Fiduciary obligation

There is a level of expectation in the legal community specifically regarding financial concerns, where a higher level of responsibility is presumed when a special relationship of trust exists between an expert and a client because of the financial consequences that may be influenced by the expert's special knowledge and insight. An expert with special knowledge and insight that may impact the client's financial well being is called a fiduciary and a fiduciary bears particular obligation to consider the financial impact of any action, advice, or information provided for the non-expert.

Fiduciary obligation is much more than the kind of warranty that would be expected for most products or services. It is a responsibility in the manner of a trusteeship, particularly with regard to the client's well being (physical and/or financial health), regarding issues the expert is addressing for the client. It is a trust of the kind that traditionally has exacted obligations beyond those associated with arms-length transactions. It is a responsibility that obliges the fiduciary to consider the consequences to the non-expert who relies on the expert's actions, advice, or opinions. In considering the consequences to the non-expert, the fiduciary is obliged to act in the best interest of said non-expert.

This point is very important and deserves reiteration. A fiduciary is legally obligated to act in the best interest of the non-expert. All actions (including inactions) of a fiduciary must be based on due consideration of the best interests of the non-expert.

The client should be able to trust that the expert he has hired will apply his expertise in the client's best interest. The application of expertise, whether it includes direct action on the client's behalf or is merely the setting out of expert opinion or advice, should also include reasonable disclosure of risks for the client.

This position of trust involving matters of individual well-being is somewhat similar to the relationship a parent has toward a child, where it is understood that the child is not capable of making some judgements so the parent is held to be responsible to the child, for the child, and to society in regard to the child. Where an expert is a fiduciary, it is presumed the client is not capable of making some judgements with regard to matters of financial concern or must make some decision(s) which may have financial consequences while relying on advice or information provided by the expert, and the hired expert is considered to be in a special position of trust with responsibility for (part of) the client's well-being.

In the event that a client suffers a financial loss because of actions taken under the guidance of or relying upon the report of a hired expert, the question may arise as to the liability of the expert with respect to those losses because of the expert's fiduciary responsibility. A key ingredient in deciding liability would be the kind of work the expert was commissioned to undertake. To what extent did the advice of the expert touch upon the financial or physical health of the non-expert who relied on the report, or to what extent did the advice of the expert influence any decision(s) the non-expert must make which may have financial or medical consequences for the non-expert? What such issues would the hypothetical reasonable person consider that the expert was addressing or should have been addressing for the client, given the job the expert was commissioned to do?

In legal terms, what is usually done by people in any calling may provide evidence of previous practice, but cannot be considered the measure of what ought to be done. The actions and procedures that are to be expected must be fixed by a standard of reasonable prudence, not by prior example. The tendency to do things "the way they are usually done" can lead to a situation where someone may feel they have been injured and initiate a lawsuit for damages. New standards of what is reasonable may then be established through litigation with one party claiming to have suffered an injury because of the action or unreasonable inaction of another. A whole calling may have lagged behind changes in the art, and the courts may be called upon to rule what is required. If, for example, a failure to disclose causes injury, the findings of the court may establish that reasonable prudence increases disclosure requirements beyond what was previously considered acceptable given the current state of the art.

For a litigation to obtain over an issue of disclosure, an un-revealed risk that should have been disclosed must materialise. This is because negligence unrelated to injury is non-actionable. Failure to disclose a risk, however unpardonable, is legally without consequence if the risk does not materialise and cause injury. There must be a causal relationship between failure to adequately disclose and damage to the plaintiff.

What could constitute injury or damage may be much broader than some people might realise. Injuries may be financial (e.g. investment loss), physical (e.g. radiation poisoning), social (e.g. damaged reputation), or personal (e.g. mental anguish).

If the duty of reasonable disclosure with respect to information of consequence to the well-being of the client is overlooked, the fiducial quality of the relationship may put the appraiser in jeopardy. The important key to what is appropriate regarding the somewhat thorny issue of disclosure is the adjective *reasonable*.

Different judges or juries who consider the time, place, circumstances, and principals concerned in any particular case may arrive at disparate interpretations of legal judgement as to what is reasonable. As a safeguard against a finding of liability for inadequate or non-disclosure arising from litigation, the most prudent approach for the expert to take is to be more than reasonable in all statements of disclosure.

There can be little doubt that fiduciary obligation accompanies a collateral appraisal, a probate appraisal, a property settlement appraisal, or a donation appraisal. The extent of fiduciary responsibility accompanying an appraisal for resale or an appraisal for insurance depends upon the particular case. That the value on any appraisal, including an appraisal for insurance, be appropriate and realistic lies within the realm of fiduciary obligation. This is made particularly clear if there is a claim for a loss on an insurance policy that is then rescinded because of an unrealistic value on the appraisal.

Whatever kind of appraisal was produced, a value that is considered unrealistic will put the onus on the appraiser to prove the opinion of value was defensible as being realistic. If the appraiser's defence is less than compelling it becomes more likely that he will be judged to have violated his fiduciary obligations.

There is also the issue of third party liability. It should be noted that the appraiser (or the company) **is responsible to any third party** who makes a decision of consequence while relying on the expert opinion regardless of never having met or made direct representation to that third party. That responsibility to third parties continues *regardless* of any blanket disclaimer. A disclaimer such as *"We assume no liability with respect to any action taken on the basis of this appraisal"* could be determined to be unreasonable because:

- o The appraiser claims special expertise, which is evidenced by the existence of the appraisal.
- o The appraiser was paid for the expert opinion, not because of the generosity of the patron toward experts in general, but because the person who commissioned the opinion intended to use that opinion as expert advice, or intended to pass that expert opinion on for someone else to use as expert advice.
- o An expert is obliged to appreciate that an expert opinion is likely to be relied upon by a non-expert to make a decision of consequence. Regardless of any assumption expressed, the courts may hold the appraiser (or his employer) liable.

A reasonable disclaimer clause on an appraisal can limit liability. It would be more defensible to say, "*We assume no liability for misuse of this appraisal and it is inappropriate to consider the value cited for any purpose other than the basis for insurance coverage. This appraisal should not influence a decision to purchase.*" This wording advises the non-expert about appropriate use of the appraisal. That is much better than trying to abrogate responsibility, which would belittle the work of the appraiser while giving little, if any, real protection because, in any event, it may not be a legally effective denial. See the three-item appraisal reproduced in the appendix (p170) for one example of a reasonable disclosure/disclaimer clause. Take care that any disclaimer used is appropriate to the type of appraisal. It would be a major blunder to include the above insurance disclaimer on a probate appraisal, for example.

If an appraisal accompanies an article offered for sale, that appraisal constitutes a warranty to whoever purchases the item.

The Canadian Guidelines with Respect to the Sale and Marketing of Diamonds, Coloured Gemstones and Pearls, 2nd Ed. 1995, published by Industry Canada, a department of the Government of Canada says: "Specific *legislation regarding warranties are laid out in the Competition Act, section 52 (see Appendix One of these Guidelines) as well as provincial legislation. Industry should be aware that in the selling, advertising, offering for sale or distribution of industry articles every statement or reference as to identity or quality or value of an article constitutes a warranty by the vendor. This principle applies in every instance and includes circumstances where the vendor quotes, makes reference to, or provides access to copies of the independent opinion of a third party, even if the vendor claims to be in dispute with the quoted opinion.*"

It may help to understand the importance of what is said if it is understood that, whether the appraiser intends it to be used that way or not, the appraisal may become a *written* warranty for that appraised item when it is sold.

Once produced and paid for, the appraisal document and the information it contains should rest solely with the owner of the appraisal. Any release of information from the document (or from the files related to the document) must be at the discretion of the owner of the appraisal. The appraiser and clerical support staff should maintain complete confidentiality, subject only to public responsibility or a court order for release of information.

When the owner of an item uses an appraisal as the basis for insurance coverage, under the principle of "utmost good faith" it must be understood that the owner has agreed to share with the insurance company all information about the insured item embodied in that appraisal. The insurer is therefore entitled to receive explanations and/or answers to queries about insured items in an appraisal to the same extent as the owner. The owner automatically authorises this by offering the appraisal as information to the insurance company and the insurance company accepts that authorization by underwriting the insurance. This does not mean, however, that the insurance company has access to the entire file, just information about insured items. They are not entitled to other information such as the telephone number or address of the insured or the insured's spouse's name, or anything else in the file other than information about the specific item(s) they actually insure.

An example of public responsibility taking precedence over privacy occurs when there are grounds to suspect that an article for which an appraisal is commissioned is stolen property. The clear obligation in this case is to notify the police of the suspicion so they can investigate on behalf of the public.

Anne Neumann, an appraiser I particularly respect and admire for her skill, diligence and integrity, felt vaguely uneasy about a diamond solitaire on which she was doing a routine appraisal. She said, "I'm sure I've seen this stone before, somewhere" and because of this vague suspicion did an extensive search of the files. Her extra research uncovered that another person with the same surname as the current client had, months previously, settled an insurance claim for loss of a diamond of similar description. The subsequent police investigation resulted in a conviction for insurance fraud.

Integrity! There is no substitute for it. It shows again and again in the minutia of daily performance and interactions with other professionals. Integrity is a consistency of attitude in conscientiously striving for honesty and justice in all dealings, a wholeness and trueness of mind set. It is demonstrated repeatedly by how one fulfills obligations and responsibilities to society, the jewellery industry, the appraising profession and the client who is the end user of the appraisal.

If one is employed by a retailer or by an appraising firm, the employer is entirely responsible to his clients while the employee is responsible to the boss. Superiors may dictate the approach, documentation, system, content, or style of the work done. They may or may not allow changes to the way things are done for that firm. Even if they allow complete free reign, it is the company that bears the full responsibility to the client (or any third party) for everything done on their behalf.

Any damage claims resulting from the handling of the goods or the content of the appraisal should be made to the company and not to the employee personally. Larger companies will likely have insurance to cover loss or damage, and may also have "errors and omissions" insurance to cover additional liabilities.

One must decide, when considering whether to accept (or continue in) a position of employment, if the way the company does things accords with one's principles. Individuals should not be held personally liable for any work done for their boss, but personal reputation is not covered by the employer's insurance. People in the industry are much more likely to consider the person whose signature is there than the name of the company when making critical judgements!

Under any arrangements other than straight employment, whether in partnership or subcontract relationship, both vendor and appraiser share responsibility to the client and may be jointly and severally liable for any errors, omissions, negligence or damages arising from the appraisal work or handling of the client's goods. It makes no difference whether the appraisal document bears a retailer's name or is the appraiser's form. The rationale for this is that the client has sought the service from the retailer (maybe relying on their good name), and the appraiser provides the service; so both are responsible. The client should be able to confidently rely on the good name of the retailer as well as the content of the appraisal.

This leads to another point regarding subcontract appraisal work. When doing appraisal work at a wholesale level for a store, such work must be maintained in files attributed to that retailer only. Even if the store provides the full name and address of its clients, that is information to be placed on the appraisal document, not an invitation to add their client to a mailing list. Integrity as a professional requires a respect for the retailer's relationship with his client. Never do any direct mailing to these clients. The only exception is if that retail establishment has gone out of business without notice of third party interest in their client list. Then the responsibility of servicing the client will default to whoever holds the records. If passage of time since the previous appraisal indicates a notice advising an update is appropriate, notify the retailer but do not directly contact the client except on the explicit instruction of the retailer.

Be straightforward and honest in all dealings but never offer gratuitous derogatory comments about competitors or individuals in the jewellery industry. That is not to say one should avoid answering direct questions or must pussyfoot about problem cases, just be prudent.

It is almost always better to say something positive rather than shoot from the hip. Harold Weinstein, when asked in a general way what he thinks of another appraiser, tends to respond that he appraises jewellery, not people. There was one occasion many years ago when a respected wholesale client was seeking a second opinion on an item already appraised by Harold's staff. He strongly pressed Harold to say something about a particular appraiser he was considering using for the second opinion. The reputation of the person under discussion was less than exemplary, we were aware of numerous instances of questionable conduct and he was currently under investigation for fraudulently issuing accommodating appraisals on new goods he had not examined. Harold's response was "He has one of the best collections of comparison stones I've seen, and I'm sorry, but that's all I have to say about him". The minimal positive comment spoke volumes about the shortcomings of the appraiser in question, while confirming the wisdom and integrity of the speaker.

Computerized appraisals

There is nothing inherently good or bad, no moral or ethical significance to computers themselves. They are merely tools that an appraiser may use: tools that can maximize productivity by doing much of the drudgery when used with knowledge, care, and awareness of the pitfalls and shortcomings. Whether their use is appropriate or not depends on the people, not on the machines. The two aspects that establish whether a computerized appraisal is valid are, first, how the computer is programmed and, second, how that program is used.

The expert

The thing to bear in mind is that (in spite of the development of the so-called "expert systems") a machine cannot generate an expert opinion. It is the person who is the expert, not the computer. The appraiser should be using the computer as an aid in arriving at an expert opinion, not relying on the machine to make decisions. It is not a valid appraisal if the "appraiser" provides the computer with measurements and quality grades so the computer can perform unknown calculations to generate the final document.

The key difference between using the machine and serving the machine lies in whether or not the user has knowledge and control of the database, the process, and each of the calculations. Of course, one must also have the will to exercise control over the machine and not be lulled into complacently using the machine's default settings for inappropriate items or purposes.

Returning to the two aspects to establish validity: first the computer programmer must create a program wherein the appraiser can freely access all of the data, processes, and calculations. Then the appraiser must understand how to, and be willing to, alter any part of the system as necessary and avoid the trap of lazily using the default settings. If one understands and agrees with the process the computer uses, and is able and willing to alter the data, the process, or any calculation as necessary, then the computer can be a very valuable tool in helping to produce a perfectly valid appraisal.

Remember that the computer programme should be set up to allow changes, not just to database information or to particular calculations, but to the process itself if necessary. Each part of the database, process, or calculations that the programme hides from the user reduces the validity of the end product as being **the appraiser's** expert opinion. Some would go so far as to say that if any part whatsoever cannot be modified then the appraisal is entirely invalidated. I empathise with that position but would suggest it is an overstatement.

Horror story

Every once in a while some journalist decides to do the standard story about inconsistencies in jewellery appraising and trots a few items around to a number of appraisers. Most such stories dwell upon variations in the values and do a less than complete job at analysing content. There are so many horror stories in the gem and jewellery industry related to appraisals that they could fill volumes. The example I present here arose because of differences in values but the real horror is in the content of the descriptions and the similarities in some values.

I once did a study and report for a Museum on appraisals the Museum had commissioned of a number of gems in their collection. The Museum gave me permission to quote from their documents (to present educational examples) provided I deleted reference to the name of the Museum and to the names of the appraisers.

On the following pages are two examples from this case. The six appraisals, three for each example stone, are reproduced complete with all their typographical errors.

In perusing these examples it will be seen that my report to the Museum pointed out most of the worst faults, but not all of the deficiencies. They include outrageously blatant examples of incompetence and idiocy that would boggle the mind of the conscientious competent appraiser.

The appraisers show various levels of competence and integrity, but all three have produced documents with seriously questionable content. The near equivalence of value between appraisers "A" and "B" (dated about the same time and having remarkably similar inaccurate descriptions of colour for the aquamarine) could cause one to consider the possibility of collusion and perhaps even conspiracy to commit fraud. In contrast, the work of appraiser C gives me no cause to express concern about his integrity, just the content of his work.

(**Not** intended as a model, duplicates all errors of an original)

APPRAISER "A" company name
List of company specialities
company address and telephone

Appraisal For:

To whom it may concern   November ##, 19##

NAME	DATE

ADDRESS

CERTIFICATE #

1) One Loose Gemstone

   Natural Beryl, Dark Blue Aquamarine

   Weight: 123.00 carats
   Color: Medium Dark Intense Blue (with a light
             tink of green wisible when viewed down
             the axis of the gem
   Clarity: Near Flawless
   Shape: Antique rectangular cushion
   Cut Quality: excellent
   Dimensions: 39mm x 27.50mm x 16.20mm

   Signature
   Appraiser's name
   Designations   Value: $ 123,000.00
   Company's seal

THIS APPRAISAL IS BASED ON ESTIMATES OF STONE QUALITY AND SIZES. WE ASSUME NO LIABILITY WITH
RESPECT TO ANY ACTION THAT MAY BE TAKEN ON THE BASIS OF THIS APPRAISAL.

(**Not** intended as a model, duplicates all errors of an original)

APPRAISER "B" company name
List of company specialities
company address and telephone

logo

NAME: TO WHOM IT MAY CONCERN

ADDRESS: DATE: Nov ##, 19##

To whom it may concern:
Number of appraised articles: One loose gemstone
ARTICLES AND DESCRIPTION

1. One loose transparent gemstone.
   Fancy rectangular mixed cushion antique facetted.
   Length of - 39.00mm. Width of - 27.50mm. Depth of - 16.20mm.
   Weight of - 123.00ct. (by balance)
   Refractive index - 1.577 - 1.583

Hexagonal growth -	Double refractive
Uniaxial - negative	Pleochroism - 2
Specific gravity - 2.72	Dispersion - .014
Relative Hardness - 7.5 - 8	

   The gemstone displays medium to dark intens blue with light tints of
   concentration of green displayed down the axies.
   I.D. - Beryl - Aquamarine

Clarity - LI/1	Tone - 75
color - 2	Proportions (finish) - 4

   Evaluation is based on current retail replacement prices   **Value: $124,000.00**

INSTRUMENTS USED

Microscope		Leveridge Gauge	
Master-Gemstones	Diamond-Lite	D.W.T. Scale	Signature
Refractometer	Polariscope	Polaroid Plate	Appraiser's name
Fluorescence	Formula	Charts	Designations
Reference	Utility lamp	Diamond balance	Company's seal

COMMENTS
Carat weight by diamond balance

APPRAISER "B" company Ltd. intend this appraisal solely for insurance purposes; made to the best of our knowledge through education in the industry and the value being a replacement retail cost of each article listed. We assume no liability.

(**Not** intended as a model, duplicates all errors of an original)

APPRAISER "C" company name
List of company specialities
company address and telephone

Name:
Address:
Date:
To whom it may concern:
Number of articles appraised:

THE - - - - MUSEUM - - - -
MUSEUM'S ADDRESS
AUGUST ##, 19##   (the following year)

1. ONE LOOSE UNMOUNTED GEMSTONE
IDENTIFICATION: NATURAL BERYL/ AQUAMARINE
CUT: MODIFIED RECTANGULAR CUSHION
LENGTH: 39.00 M.M.
WIDTH: 26.30 M.M.
CARAT WEIGHT: 122.98 CARATS
CLARITY: VERY VERY LIGHTLY INCLUDED
COLOUR: CYAN/ 20/10% /B/G /CM MEDIUM VERY SLIGHTLY GREENISH BLUE
CUT & POLISH: VERY GOOD
REPLACEMENT VALUE: $ 95, 680.00

Signature
Appraiser's name
Designations
Company's seal

chart of diamond clarity grading scale - - - - - - - - - -

chart of GIA COLOR GRADING SCALE (for diamonds) - - - - - - - -

APPRAISER's company Ltd. make the above appraisal to the best of their knowledge and belief, but assume no liability. This appraisal is for insurance purpose only, being an estimate of the cost to replace the articles listed as current retail prices at this date.

APPRAISER "A" company name
List of company specialities
company address and telephone

Appraisal For:

To whom it may concern   November ##, 19##

NAME   DATE

ADDRESS

CERTIFICATE #

1)   One Loose Gemstone

Natural CHRYSOBERYL, CATS-EYE-ALEXANDRITE

Weight: 8.40 carats
Color: Medium Dark Brownish Green
Clarity: Included
Shape: Round Encabochon Cut
Cut Quality: Good
Dimensions: 10mm round x 8.2mm deep
Phenomina: Excellent Blue White
            Chatoyancy; Poor, just
            perceptible color change

            Signature
        Appraiser's name
           Designations   Value: $ 84,000.00
         Company's seal

N.B.; This Gem exhibits the best example of Chrysoberyl
Chatoyancy ever witnessed by this appraiser in a stone
of this size.   (appraiser's initials)

THIS APPRAISAL IS BASED ON ESTIMATES OF STONE QUALITY AND SIZES. WE ASSUME NO LIABILITY WITH
RESPECT TO ANY ACTION THAT MAY BE TAKEN ON THE BASIS OF THIS APPRAISAL.

(**Not** intended as a model, duplicates all errors of an original)

APPRAISER "B" company name
List of company specialities
company address and telephone

logo

NAME: TO WHOM IT MAY CONCERN

ADDRESS: DATE: Nov ##, 19##

To whom it may concern:
Number of appraised articles: One loose gemstone

ARTICLES AND DESCRIPTION

---

1. One loose translucent to opague gemstone.
    Fancy round en cabochon cut.
    Diameter of - 10.00mm.   Depth of - 8.20mm.
    Weight of - 8.40ct. (by balance)
    Refractive index - spot 1.745
    Double refractive   Biaxial - positive
    Specific gravity - 3.73   Orthorhombic
    Phenomina - play of colour Hardness - 8 1/2
    I.D. - Chrysoberyl/Cats eye Alexandrite

    Value: $85,300.00

    Evaluation is based on current retail replacement prices

    INSTRUMENTS USED

Microscope		Leveridge Gauge
Master-Gemstones	Diamond-Lite	D.W.T. Scale
Refractometer	Polariscope	Polaroid Plate
Fluorescence	Formula	Charts
Reference	Utility lamp	Diamond balance

Signature
Appraiser's name
Designations
Company's seal

COMMENTS
Carat weight by diamond balance

APPRAISER "B" company Ltd. intend this appraisal solely for insurance purposes; made to the best of our knowledge through education in the industry and the value being a replacement retail cost of each article listed. We assume no liability.

---

*(**Not** intended as a model, duplicates all errors of an original)*

APPRAISER "C" company name
List of company specialities
company address and telephone

Name:
Address:
Date:
To whom it may concern:
Number of articles appraised:

THE - - - - MUSEUM - - - -
MUSEUM'S ADDRESS
AUGUST ##, 19##   *(the following year)*

1. ONE LOOSE UNMOUNTED GEMSTONE
IDENTIFICATION: NATURAL CHRYSOBERYL / CATSEYE ALEXANDRITE
CUT: OVAL CABOCHON
LENGTH: 10.50 M.M.
WIDTH: 8.20 M.M.
CARAT WEIGHT: 8.42 CARATS
CLARITY: SOME FRACTURES BREAK SURFACE, VERY HEAVILY INCLUDED
COLOUR CHANGE: POOR/ FAIR
CHATOYANCY: VERY GOOD
COLOUR: MEDIUM GREYISH BROWN GREEN
REPLACEMENT VALUE: $ 29,950.00

Signature
Appraiser's name
Designations
Company's seal

chart of diamond clarity grading scale - - - - - - - - - -

chart of GIA COLOR GRADING SCALE (for diamonds) - - - - - - - -

APPRAISER's company Ltd. make the above appraisal to the best of their knowledge and belief, but assume no liability. This appraisal is for insurance purpose only, being an estimate of the cost to replace the articles listed as current retail prices at this date.

Comments regarding H#1

Spiral-cut sharp cornered almost rectangular cushion shaped aquamarine, 123.00 carats \ 122.98 carats;

- Appraised by "APPRAISER A" for $123,000.00 … this valuation seems reasonable as a fair market value even though it is only specified as "value", which is vague. The description is hardly adequate, a "Medium Dark" tone or "Dark Blue" is very exceptional in aquamarine (and does not conform to the photograph of this stone) and the clarity grade "Near Flawless" is suspect, a non-standard term in disagreement with the other two appraisals. Style of cut should be mentioned, not just shape. The appraisal should not be addressed "To whom it may concern".

- Appraised by "APPRAISER B" for $124,000.00 … this value seems reasonable (although curiously close in conformity with the previous appraisal) as a fair market value but it should not be specified as "retail replacement" which implies it is readily replaceable. Much information in the description is superfluous and copied from reference materials to pad the document and make it look more impressive (refractive index, hexagonal growth, uniaxial-negative, specific gravity, dispersion, hardness); it would require an extraordinary gemmology laboratory to measure dispersion and would require monumental ignorance and stupidity to do a hardness test! Some information is in non-standard terminology that makes no sense to me (i.e. proportions-4, color-2, tone-75, pleochroism-2). The appraisal should not be addressed "To whom it may concern".

- Appraised by "APPRAISER C" for $95,680.00 … although there are more significant digits in the value than can be justified by the accuracy of appraisals this valuation seems reasonable as a fair market value, but it should not be specified as "replacement value" which implies it is readily replaceable. The description is marginal; the cut only indicates the outline shape, the notation of clarity uses non-standard terminology, and the colour is difficult to interpret.

Comments regarding EXAMPLE H#2

Alexandrite cat's eye, 8.40 carats \ 8.42 carats;

o   Appraised by "APPRAISER A" for $84,000.00 … this valuation seems very high for fair market value (considering the descriptions of the colour change on all the appraisals). The description is marginal, colour and clarity are incomplete or use non-standard terminology (there should be separate descriptions of hue, tone and purity for the colour under each of two types of lighting) and there is no indication of the degree of transparency. The N.B. causes me to wonder how many 8 1/2 carat cymophanes this appraiser has examined! The statement would be correct even if he has only seen this one, which reduces credibility of his implied experience.

o   Appraised by "APPRAISER B" for $85,300.00 … this valuation seems very high (and curiously close in conformity with the previous appraisal) for fair market value (considering the descriptions of the colour change on all the appraisals). The description is filled with errors in terminology and pointless padding. To say an alexandrite cat's eye exhibits "play of colour" is a wild misunderstanding of the term since any gemmologist should know that play of colour refers to the phenomenon exhibited by precious opal. This unhelpful description has no details of colours, clarity, quality of chatoyancy or quality of cut. The stone is called "translucent to opaque" (sic), which implies a gradation from translucent to opaque although I suspect that sub-translucent was intended. The appraiser names the style of cut as "fancy round en cabochon" although the word "fancy" is no more relevant to cabochon than it is to round.

o   Appraised by "APPRAISER C" for $29,950.00 … although there are more significant digits in the value than can be justified by the accuracy of appraisals this valuation seems reasonable as a fair market value, but it should not be specified as "replacement value" which implies it is ready replaceable. The description is marginal, colour and clarity are incomplete or use non-standard terminology (there should be separate descriptions of hue, tone and purity for the colour under each of two types of lighting) and there is no indication of the degree of transparency or the quality of cut (make).

As an alexandrite this stone does not sound to be of "museum quality" although it does sound to be a reasonably good quality stone in terms of its chatoyancy and for this phenomenon could be suitable as a collection stone. The valuation by "APPRAISER A" would seem appropriate for a stone with much better colour change phenomenon. The valuation by "APPRAISER C" seems more realistic.

Appendices

Most of the information set out in these appendices are example blank work sheets, formulae, lists, and charts. Explanations here are generally limited to notes to the worksheets for the three-item example appraisal.

Setting up a laboratory

When setting up a laboratory for performing jewellery valuations, careful planning will minimize difficulties. It will be much easier to do a competent job with the appropriate resources, equipment and environment.

Location

The environment in which one works can profoundly influence the ability to perform. If working on site, there will be limiting conditions worthy of note in the appraisal, but one should minimise shortcomings as much as possible. If setting up an appraising laboratory here are some points to consider:
- Colours of walls, ceiling, flooring, curtains, and furnishings, should be white, neutral grey, or black.
- Flooring should be of resilient material such as carpet or linoleum, not concrete or ceramic tile.
- Light should be completely controlled. A darkroom environment is ideal but if the room has a window it should face away from the noonday sun and have adequate shades or curtains to block out early morning or late afternoon sun.

- Ventilation should be adequate for use of diiodomethane immersion testing for diffusion treated corundums, ammonia in cleaning, acetone swab testing, and the various other fluids used in specific gravity testing or other applications.
- The environment should be comfortable and quiet without loud noises or visual distractions.
- Privacy is important for security and is also psychologically important in a work environment. Few people work at their best under continuous scrutiny.
- Access to sufficient electrical supply to operate equipment is important. Most gemmology equipment is quite low wattage, essentially just lights of one sort or another, but cleaning equipment such as a heavy duty ultrasonic cleaner or particularly a steam cleaner may be best served with a separately fused dedicated circuit.
- Plumbing may not usually be thought of as a major gemmology consideration, but an available sink can be very helpful with a steam cleaner and ultrasonic cleaner, and can be a factor for anything from small spills and accidents to medical emergencies. Make sure the drain opening is covered with a fine screen when emptying the ultrasonic unit or rinsing off cleaned jewellery.
- An appraising laboratory can be compactly organised but should not be squeezed into an uncomfortably tight environment. The space should be adequate to allow the appraiser flexibility in positioning of equipment and materials.

Equipment

An adequately equipped jewellery-appraising laboratory will include most of the following items of equipment:
- binocular dark field microscope
- carat scale
- Chelsea filter and other colour filters
- coloured stone grading light (5000°K or 4500°K incandescent, or a "daylight" fluorescent with a high colour rendering index)
- diamond grading light
- dichroscope
- electrochemical metal tester
- fibre-optic light

- o   fluorescent desk lamp (straight tube type)
- o   gram scale
- o   immersion cell
- o   immersion liquids
- o   infra-red reflectometer
- o   Leveridge gauge
- o   long and short wave ultraviolet light
- o   loupe
- o   measuring tape
- o   microscope graticule
- o   millimetre micrometer
- o   polariscope
- o   polarizing filter
- o   quartz-halogen pen-light (pocket torch)
- o   refractometer
- o   scintillometer
- o   sodium light or narrow bandwidth yellow filter
- o   specific gravity liquids
- o   spectroscope
- o   steam cleaner
- o   table gauge
- o   thermal inertia tester
- o   thermal reaction tester
- o   touchstone type metal testing kit
- o   tweezers
- o   ultrasonic cleaner
- o   vernier callipers.

Grading resources

In addition to equipment one must also have comparison standards for grading diamonds, coloured gemstones, and pearls. At a minimum one should have:
- o   diamond colour grading masters
- o   pearl grading masters
- o   colour description standards.

The master stones used for colour grading diamonds should be non-fluorescing Cape series diamonds of good make. Higher clarity stones are much preferred but SI stones with no dark or coloured inclusions may be acceptable. About 0.30 to 0.36 ct stones are useful for grading a range of diamond sizes. A top E or bottom D is the preferred highest colour master, and if one has a master at the alternate cusps between lower grades (such as a top G, top I, and top K) one will have an ideal set for accurate colour grading.

Cubic zirconia "diamond grading masters" are not recommended for a few reasons:
- The colour in yellow CZ may not be stable
- CZ is of a slightly different hue than Cape series diamond
- Most importantly, the lustre of CZ is pronouncedly different than the lustre of diamond.

This lustre difference is of particular significance in the higher colour grades where the difference in colour between grades is so subtle it may be difficult to judge whether the difference in appearance between the stone being tested and the master is a difference in tone, hue, or lustre. With Cape series diamond masters all such problems are eliminated when grading the typically common Cape series diamonds, and there are never lustre differences regardless of hue.

Commercially available pearl grading masters will help make pearl grading much more consistent than trying to grade by just observation and memory. The somewhat limited commercial set can be expanded and refined as time and opportunity allow.

Standard colour references may vary from simple printed colour grids, to transparent coloured films, to imitation or synthetic gemstones, to genuine gemstone comparison masters. Some Registered Valuers in the U.K. have purchased commercially offered genuine gemstone comparison masters.

Example worksheets

Appraisal Worksheet

Job # _____

Client of: _____ ref. # _____

NAME: _____ DATE: _____ METAL $_____

ADDRESS: _____ K __9, __10, __14, __18, __22, __PLAT

_____ yellow, ___white, ___tricolour

_____ other_____

TELEPHONE: _____

ITEM DESCTIPTION: _____

_____

_____

_____

MARKS or STAMPINGS: _____ GROSS GRAMS:_____

STONE(S) _____

mm _____

CARAT(S) _____

COLOUR _____

CLARITY _____

MAKE _____

QUALITY _____

comments _____

$/ct _____

$ stone(s) _____

Mount, grams net: _____

Mount cost: ($_____ x 1.4 + _____) x 1.3 _____ = _____

raw metal   labour   setting

TOTAL COSTS = _____

ADDITIONAL COMMENTS, TESTS, ETC.

x 1.1 (excise) = _____

add mark-up > _____

round off value _____

(value excludes retail taxes)

Pearl Worksheet   Job # _____

FORMAT: length, type of item, number, dimension(s), variation, shape, type, source, colour, overtones, orient lustre, complexion, matching, nacre thickness, how strung, attachment to clasp, the clasp, & gross weight.

ITEM LENGTH: _____ cm (_____ ")   GROSS WEIGHT: _____ gm

TYPE of ITEM: #___strands, __Bracelet, ___ Necklace, ___ Choker (15"), __ Standard (18"), ___ Matinee (22")
__ Opera (30"), __ Rope (40"+), __ Graduated 3 to 6mm>>16", 3/ to 7mm>>17", 4 to 8mm>>18", 6 to 9mm>>19"
Strand Length(s):_____, Count(s):_____, Sizes:_____

Variation	Shape		Type	Source	Colour
Full drilled	Drop	Button	Bead nucleated	Cultured	White
Half drilled	Oval	Potato	Tissue nucleated	Natural	Crème
Undrilled	(10) Round	Rice	Freshwater		Rosé
3/4 cut	(7, 8, 9) Round-	Long drop	Mabé		Yellow
Dyed	-in-most	Long stick	Keshi		Silver
Fancy	(4, 5, 6) Slightly-	Fancy shape	Blister		Grey
colour	off-round	(name of shape)	Conch		Blue
Natural	(2, 3) Off-round				(modifiers or
	(1) Irregular				variations
	Baroque				of these)
	Heavily baroque				

Overtones	Orient	Lustre	Complexion	Matching	Nacre Thickness
Crème	None (0%)	Dull (1, 2)	Spotless (10)	Poor (1, 2)	Below standard (B) (1)
Rosé	Perceptible (10%)	Low (3, 4)	V. lightly (9, 8)	Fair (3, 4)	Standard (S) (2, 3)
Green	Noticeable (20%)	Medium (5, 6)	spotted	Good (5, 6)	(0.15 mm)
Blue	Significant (30%)	Bright (7, 8)	Lightly (7, 6, 5)	V. good (7, 8)	Standard+ (S+) (4, 5, 6)
(other)	Strong (40%)	Very (9, 10)	spotted	Excellent (9, 10)	(0.30 to 0.45 mm)
	Very (50%)	bright	Spotted (4, 3)		Medium-thick (M) (7, 8, 9)
	strong		Heavily (2)		(0.45 to 0.60 mm)
	orient bonus		spotted		Thick (T) (10)
	approximates as		V. heavily (1)		(0.60 to 0.90 mm)
	(10 - subtotal) x %		spotted		Very thick (V) (10+)
					(>0.90 mm)

Colour Grade   (North American market)   **colour/overtones**

10, 9	9, 8	8, 7	7, 6	6, 5	5, 4	4, 3	3, 2	2, 1
pink/rosé		white/none		crème/rosé		crème/green		yellow/none
	pink/none		light grey/rosé	crème/none			gold/rosé	
white/rosé		light crème/rosé			dark crème/none			gold/none
	black/rosé		light crème/none	dark crème/rosé		silver/rosé		
black/green				white/green				grey
		faint gray/rosé				dark crème/green		

Colour Grade @ 0.10,   complexion @ 0.20,   Nacre @ 0.25,   Orient bonus
shape @ 0.15,   Lustre @ 0.25,   Matching @ 0.05,   Subtotal,   grade total

_____ + _____ + _____ + _____ + _____ + _____ = _____ + _____ = _____

OVERALL QUALITY GRADE: 1 - 4 commercial, 4 - 6 good, 6 - 8 fine, 8 - 10 extra fine

___ Knotted, ___ Continuous, ___ French wire, ___Bead tip, ___ Clam-shell tip,

CLASP: _____

pearls cost: _____, clasp cost: _____, assembly cost: _____, total: _____

APPRAISER:

Opal Worksheet (after Paul Downing)

Length _____, **Width** _____, **Depth** _____, **Weight**: _____ct

I. **Type** of opal: Solid ___, **Boulder** ___, Matrix ___, Treated___, Assembled ____, Synthetic___, Simulant ___

II. **Base** colour: Black___, **Black** Crystal___, Semi Black___, Grey___, White ___, Semi Crystal ___, Crystal ____
Boulder Black ___, Boulder Brown ___, Boulder White ___, Orange ___, Other _____

III. **Brightness:** of play of colour: 1___subdued, 2___medium, 3___bright, 4___very bright, 5___shade vivid

IV. **Size:** for Boulder opal
_____Small <5 ct, _____ Medium <10 ct, _____ Large <15 ct, _____ Very Large <30 ct, _____ V. V. Large
<100 mm^2 <200 mm^2 <300 mm^2 <600 mm^2 >600 mm^2

V. **Price Range:** {from guide} _____ to _____, **Base Price** _____, **Spread** _____
                         {midpoint of range}   {highest minus lowest}

VI. **Additions/Subtractions:**   white and others,   (blacks)

    Colours: in play Blue only (-.50), Green only -.10 (-.20), Blue-Green -.05 (-.10)
        Green-Orange +.00 (+.10), Orange-green +.05 (+.15), Red Only +.05 (+.25), Orange-Red +.10 (+.30)
        Green-Blue -.00 (-.10), Multicolour +.10 (+.30), Red Multi +.20 (+.40), Red-Blue Multi +.25 (+.50)

    Pattern: in play, Pinfire (-.05), Mixed Flash (-.00), Broad Flash (-.00) Rolling Flash (+.10)
        Harlequin (+.20), Rare Patterns & Picture Stones (+.00 to + .20)

    Shape: Standard oval +.15 (+.00), free size oval (-.00), other standard shape -.00 (-.20),
    carvings (+.10 to -.30)

    Dome: low dome (-.10),   medium dome (+.00),   high dome +.10 (+.20)

    Finish: poor finish, such as irregular dome, buff top, poor polish, etc.   (-.10 to -.50)

    Inclusions: FI (+.00),   LI (-.15),   MI to HI (-.20 to -.50)

    Consistency: of pattern & brightness Consistent (-.00), Major dull spot (-.20), Minor dull spot (-.10)
        Undesirable pattern mix (-.20), Distracting variation in base colour (-.20)

    Directionality: Not directional (+.10),   Slightly directional (-.00)
    Somewhat directional (-.05),   Very directional (-.20),   Highly Directional (-.30)

    Size {*finest quality large* are *deducted less*} to 0.49 ct -.30 (-.50), 0.50 to 0.99 ct -.20 (-.30)
    15.00 to 19.99 ct (-.15), 20.00 to 29.99 ct (-.20), 0.30 to 39.99 ct (-.25), 40.00 ct & over (-.30)

VII. **Base Price Adjustment**
    TOTAL Additions/Subtractions_____ **X** Price Spread_____ = _____

VIII. **Adjusted Base Price** Base Price_____ + Base Price Adjustment_____ = _____

IX. **Total Estimated Price** For an "each" price use the Adjusted Base Price for the stone.

    For a per carat priced stone: Adjusted Base Price _____ **X** ct_____ = _____

X. **Final Review & Adjustment**
    Consider the calculated price and adjust if necessary _____ (giving reasons below)

OPAL WORK SHEET (after Barrie O'Leary)

mm SIZE_____   shape _____   _____ ct

make comments _____

OPAL TYPE: (one only)			1 = 2/8000	26 = 7/400	51 = 21/80	76 = 46/80
BLACK	+30		2 = 3/8000	27 = 8/400	52 = 22/80	77 = 47/80
BLACK CRYSTAL	+20		3 = 4/8000	28 = 9/400	53 = 23/80	78 = 48/80
SEMI BLACK	+15		4 = 5/8000	29 = 5/200	54 = 24/80	79 = 49/80
CRYSTAL	+10		5 = 6/8000	30 = 6/200	55 = 25/80	80 = 50/80
FIRE	+10		6 = 7/8000	31 = 7/200	56 = 26/80	81 = 51/80
TOP WHITE	+10		7 = 8/8000	32 = 8/200	57 = 27/80	82 = 52/80
GREY	+5		8 = 3/2000	33 = 9/200	58 = 28/80	83 = 53/80
LIGHT	+5		9 = 4/2000	34 = 4/80	59 = 29/80	84 = 54/80
BOULDER	+5	____	10 = 5/2000	35 = 5/80	60 = 30/80	85 = 55/80
PROMINENT COLOURS: (all)			11 = 6/2000	36 = 6/80	61 = 31/80	86 = 56/80
RED	+30	____	12 = 7/2000	37 = 7/80	62 = 32/80	87 = 57/80
ORANGE	+15	____	13 = 8/2000	38 = 8/80	63 = 33/80	88 = 58/80
GREEN	+10	____	14 = 9/2000	39 = 9/80	64 = 34/80	89 = 59/80
BLUE	+5	____	15 = 5/1000	40 = 10/80	65 = 35/80	90 = 30/40
VIOLET	+5	____	16 = 6/1000	41 = 11/80	66 = 36/80	91 = 31/40
PURPLE	+5	____	17 = 7/1000	42 = 12/80	67 = 37/80	92 = 32/40
COLOUR BONUS:			18 = 8/1000	43 = 13/80	68 = 38/80	93 = 33/40
RED/BLUE	+6	____	19 = 9/1000	44 = 14/80	69 = 39/80	94 = 34/40
OPPOSITES	+5	____	20 = 10/1000	45 = 15/80	70 = 40/80	95 = 35/40
PATTERN: (1 = ¼ of face)			21 = 11/1000	46 = 16/80	71 = 41/80	96 = 36/40
PATTERN SIZE	+4	____	22 = 12/1000	47 = 17/80	72 = 42/80	97 = 37/40
PATTERN PURITY	+4	____	23 = 13/1000	48 = 18/80	73 = 43/80	98 = 38/40
BRILLIANCE:			24 = 14/1000	49 = 19/80	74 = 44/80	99 = 39/40
subdued	+1 \		25 = 6/400	50 = 20/80	75 = 45/80	100 = TOP $

BRILLIANCE:
subdued   +1 \
medium   +2 \
bright   +3 >>> ____
very bright +4 /
shade vivid +5 /
if **two** of 3 above
  is 4 add BONUS   +2   ____
TRUENESS: +6   ____
(nil if all extinction)
DEDUCTIONS:
  ODD SHAPE   -10   ____
  DEAD SPOT @ ⁴/₄ -40   ____
  POTCH @ ²/₂   -20   ____
  CRACK @ ²/₂   -20   ____
  FACE MATRIX #1   -20   ____
  FACE MATRIX #2   -40   ____
  BACK MATRIX (if back is
  all colour) @ ⁴/₄ -4   ____
         TOTAL   ____
  FLAT FACE X 1/3   ____

_____

_____

_____

_____

_____

_____

_____

Diamond colour grading systems

GIA	AGS	traditional	SCAN.D.N descriptive	less detailed	IDC	U.K.
D	0	River	Rarest White	White	exceptional white +	finest white
E					exceptional white	
F	1	Top Wesselton	Rare White		rare white +	fine white
G					rare white	
H	2	Wesselton	White		White	White
I		Top Crystal	Slightly Tinted White		slightly tinted white	commercial white
J	3	Crystal				top silver cape
K		Top Cape	Tinted White		tinted white	silver cape
L	4					
M		Cape	Slightly Yellowish			light cape
N	5					
O			Yellowish	Tinted Colour	tinted colour	
P	6	Light Yellow				cape
Q						
R	7					
S		Yellow	Yellow			dark cape
T to Z	8 to 10					

GIA: Gemological Institute of America
AGS: American Gem Society
Scan.D.N.: Scandinavian Diamond Nomenclature
IDC: International Diamond Council
U.K.: United Kingdom

(from Diamonds, by E. Bruton)

SETTING CHARGES

You will have to check the wholesale market for yourself to find out what setting charges actually are, to keep costing current.

The following setting charges are offered as an example chart.

CENTRE DIAMONDS			CLAWSET SIDES			BEAD, CHANNEL, STAR	
carat weight	$ each		carat weight	$ each		carat weight	$ each
<0.05	3.00		<0.06	3.00		to 0.03	3.75
<0.19	4.00		<0.17	3.50		to 0.05	5.50
<0.29	4.50		>0.17	4.00		to 0.12	7.25
<0.49	5.25					to 0.30	9.00
<0.75	6.00					>0.30	12.00
<1.00	9.00						
<1.50	10.50						
<2.00	12.00						
<3.00	13.50						

COLLET SET or FANCY SHAPE SHOULDERS $5.75 each

INVISIBLE SET   as centre stones + 150%_(@ centre stone x 2.5)
                  (not including cost of cutting mounting grooves in the stones)

PIN SET $2.00 each

COLOURED CENTRE STONES
Round $7.00
Other shape $8.25
Production run $4.75
Pearl gluing $0.75

FOR PLATINUM SETTINGS, FIVE TIMES THE ABOVE CHARGES (or more)

Jewellery Appraising
Example Fee Structure

Minimum of $45.00 the first item

basic charge to which any surcharge is added:

appraised items	$35.00 each
identification only	$15.00 each

Special items appraisal *surcharges*

Each stone in an item more than twenty	$1.00
Each charm on a bracelet over five	$2.00
Each gem variety over two in an article	$5.00
Each 0.50 carat or major part thereof of diamond(s) over 1.06 carat	$5.00
Each 1.00 carat or major part thereof of coloured gem over 1.06 carat	$5.00
Each item with pearl (including cultured & imitation)	$5.00
Each watch set with diamonds	$15.00
Each named designer article	$20.00
Each antique article	$20.00

Gemstone carvings, silverware, coins, etcetera, charges will be based upon the number of items and the research required, however all charges will be agreed prior to any work being started.

Property of: Mr. & Mrs. Owner
99 Good Street,
Anytown, Canada. A1B 2C3
Telephone: ....

May 26th, 1996
No. ###-##-##
Client of: **JEWELLERY STORE's NAME**
Reference: *STORE's order #*

Gold @ $550.00/oz. Cdn.

Estimated Value
Excluding Retail Sales Taxes

#1 ENGAGEMENT RING

One 14 Karat yellow and white gold size 7¼ engagement ring with half round shank, tulip shoulders, and four-prong closed-back Tiffany setting containing:
- one round brilliant cut diamond 9.64 - 8.70 x (estimated) 5.6mm, weighing approximately 3.13 carats, of H-I colour, SI_1 clarity and good make with 44% pavilion and thin polished girdle.

The ring has a total gross weight of 3.6 grams, is stamped "14K", and trademarked "F" within a diamond profile. Under ultraviolet light the diamond exhibits bright blue fluorescence and moderate yellow phosphorescence.

$45,000.00
Retail Replacement Value

#2 TOPAZ & DIAMOND RING

One hand-made 14 Karat yellow and white gold size 7 lady's dress ring with open-back four-prong yellow gold centre setting and white gold column-style side settings, containing:
- one oval facetted "imperial" topaz 9.12 x 7.83 x 5.42mm, weighing approximately 3.01 carats of strong medium orange-yellow colour, FI (VS_1) clarity and very good make;
- and two round brilliant cut diamonds 2.4mm diameter, weighing in total approximately 0.10 carat, of I-J colour, SI clarity and very good make.

The ring has a total gross weight of 3.9 grams, and is marked "14K" and "MGJ".

$3,500.00
Retail Replacement Value

#3 CULTURED PEARL NECKLACE

One 43cm (17") necklace of forty-six (46) 7.52 to 7.99 mm full drilled, round, bead nucleated cultured pearls of light crème to rosé colour with light rosé, crème and very slightly greenish overtones, perceptible orient, medium lustre, light spotting, fair matching, and medium-thick nacre, individually knotted on scalloped cup tips attached to a 14 x 18 mm 18 Karat yellow gold oval spiral fishhook style box clasp. The necklace has a total gross weight of 34.1 grams and the clasp is marked "750" within a rhombus and "*140 AR".

$6,500.00
Retail Replacement Value

THREE ITEMS .... TOTAL **$55,000.00**

This appraisal is our opinion of the authenticity, design, composition, qualities of and level of insurance appropriate for the item(s) appraised, and "*retail replacement value*" assumes replacement by the client's choice of retailer. Weights, dimensions, and quality grades are estimated with judgements limited by the mountings unless it is specifically stated the stones were examined while un-mounted. Metal qualities are reported as stampings indicate unless stated as "tested". Unless specified otherwise each described article is neither new, dangerously worn, nor damaged and may show wear typical of regularly used articles. Identity, quantification and value conclusions are made to the best of the appraiser's belief and experience within the limits of the circumstances of examination, based on judgements of quality, workmanship and costs, with bracketed grades priced at the centre (or just above) grade unless otherwise stated. An appraisal is neither an offer to buy nor sell. We assume no liability whatever for misuse of this appraisal and **it is inappropriate to consider the value cited for any purpose other than the basis for insurance coverage**. This appraisal should not be used to influence a decision to purchase any item.

signature: Richard H. Cartier, FGA, FCGmA

Appraisal Worksheet

Job # _____

Client of: ____ ✓

ref. # ___item 1___

NAME: ___Mr & Mrs Owner___ DATE: ___May 26 '96___ METAL $ ___G = 550 Cdn___

ADDRESS: ___99 Good St.,___ K ___9, ___10, (14,) ___18, ___22, ___PLAT

___Anytown, Canada,___ (yellow, ___white,) ___tricolour

___A1B 2C3___ other _____

TELEPHONE: _____

ITEM DESCTIPTION: ___size 7 1/4, L's solit., half-round shank___

___tulip shoulders, 4-P Tiffany closed-back setting___

MARKS or STAMPINGS: ___"⟨F⟩14K"___   GROSS GRAMS: ___3.629___

STONE(S)   (1) rbc dia.

mm   9.64 to 9.70 x (est.) 5.6

CARAT(S)   3.13   (@ less 2% for thin crown)

COLOUR   H-I   bright B fluo., mod. Y phosph.

CLARITY   SI-1

MAKE   good (~44% pav., thin polished girdle, thin crown)

QUALITY

comments

$/ct   6700 / 0.73 >9178

$ stone(s)   28 727.14

Mount, grams net: ___3.003___

Mount cost: ($___31.00___ x 1.4 + ___35___) x 1.3 ___+ 13___ = ___115___
                  raw metal   labour   setting

TOTAL COSTS = ___28 842___

ADDITIONAL COMMENTS, TESTS, ETC.

x 1.1 (excise) = ___31 726___

add mark-up > ___45 513___

round off value ___45 000.00___
(value excludes retail taxes)

APPRAISER: _____

Professional Jewellery Appraising   171

Appraisal Worksheet

Client of: _____ ✓

NAME: _Mr & Mrs Owner_   DATE: _May 26 '96_

ADDRESS: _____

_____

TELEPHONE: _____

ITEM DESCTIPTION: _size 7. L's dress ring, handmade,_

4-PY open back centre, column style 4-PW sides

Job # _____

ref. # _item 2_

METAL $ _____

K __9, __10, (14,) __18, __22, __PLAT

(__yellow, __white, __tricolour)

other _____

MARKS or STAMPINGS: _"14K" & MGJ"_   GROSS GRAMS: _3.946_

	STONE(S) (1) _faceted_ _oval mixed cut_ "imperial" topaz	(2) _rbc dia._
mm	9.12 x 7.83 x 5.42	2.4 D
CARAT(S)	3.01	0.10
COLOUR	strong med. OY 6	I-J nil fluo./ vs B fluo.
CLARITY	FI (VS-1) 9	SI
MAKE	vg 8	vg
QUALITY	fine	fine
comments		make premium 20%
$/ct	500 - 200)/2 x 0.5 + 200)/0.73 ~ 377	450/0.73 x 1.2 ~ 740
$ stone(s)	1134.77	74.00

Mount, grams net: _3.324_

Mount cost: ($_34.30_ x 1.4 + _140_) x 1.3 _+ 14.50_ = _202.53_
             raw metal   labour   setting

TOTAL COSTS = _1411.30_

ADDITIONAL COMMENTS, TESTS, ETC.

x 1.1 (excise) = _1552.42_

add mark-up > _3449.61_

round off value _3500.00_
(value excludes retail taxes)

APPRAISER: _____

May 26 '96   Pearl Worksheet   Job # ___Item 3, Mrs Owner___

FORMAT: length, type of item, number, dimension(s), variation, shape, type, source, colour, overtones, orient lustre, complexion, matching, nacre thickness, how strung, attachment to clasp, the clasp, & gross weight.

ITEM LENGTH: _____43_____ cm (_____17_____ ")   GROSS WEIGHT: __34.1__ gm

TYPE of ITEM: #___strands, __Bracelet, (Necklace) __ Choker (15"), __ Standard (18"), ___ Matinee (22")
__ Opera (30"), __ Rope (40"+), __ Graduated 3 to 6mm>>16", 3/ to 7mm>>17", 4 to 8mm>>18", 6 to 9mm>>19"
Strand Length(s):_____, Count(s): (46)_____, Sizes: _7.52 to 7.99_

Variation	Shape		Type	Source	Colour
(Full drilled)	Drop	Button	(Bead nucleated)	(Cultured)	White
Half drilled	Oval	Potato	Tissue nucleated	Natural	Crème
Undrilled	(10) Round	Rice	Freshwater	*light*	(Rosé)
3/4 cut	(7, 8, 9) Round-	Long drop	Mabé	*to*	Yellow
Dyed	-in-most	Long stick	Keshi		Silver
Fancy	(4, 5, 6) Slightly-	Fancy shape	Blister		Grey
colour	off-round	(name of shape)	Conch		Blue
Natural	(2, 3) Off-round				(modifiers or
	(1) Irregular				variations
	Baroque				of these)
	Heavily baroque				

Overtones	Orient	Lustre	Complexion	Matching	Nacre Thickness
(Crème) *light*	None (0%)	Dull (1, 2)	Spotless (10)	Poor (1, 2)	Below standard (B) (1)
(Rosé)	(Perceptible (10%))	Low (3, 4)	V. lightly (9, 8)	Fair (3, (4))	Standard (S) (2, 3)
(Green) *v.s.*	Noticeable (20%)	Medium (5, (6))	spotted	Good (5, 6)	(0.15 mm)
Blue	Significant (30%)	Bright (7, 8)	Lightly ((7), 6, 5)	V. good (7, 8)	Standard+ (S+) (4, 5, 6)
(other)	Strong (40%)	Very (9, 10)	spotted	Excellent (9, 10)	(0.30 to 0.45 mm)
	Very (50%)	bright	Spotted (4, 3)		Medium-thick (M) (7, (8), 9)
	strong		Heavily (2)		(0.45 to 0.60 mm)
			spotted		Thick (T) (10)
	orient bonus		V. heavily (1)		(0.60 to 0.90 mm)
	approximates as		spotted		Very thick (V) (10+)
	(10 - subtotal) x %				(>0.90 mm)

Colour Grade (North American market)   colour/overtones

10, 9	9, 8	8, (7)	7, 6	6, 5	5, 4	4, 3	3, 2	2, 1
pink/rosé		white/none		crème/rosé		crème/green		yellow/none
	pink/none		light grey/rosé		crème/none		gold/rosé	
white/rosé		light crème/rosé				dark crème/none		gold/none
	black/rosé		light crème/none		dark crème/rosé		silver/rosé	
black/green				white/green				grey
		faint gray/rosé				dark crème/green		

Colour Grade @ 0.10,   complexion @ 0.20,   Nacre @ 0.25,   Orient bonus
shape @ 0.15,   Lustre @ 0.25,   Matching @ 0.05,   Subtotal,   grade total

_1.5_ + _0.7_ + _1.5_ + _1.4_ + _0.2_ + _2.0_ = _7.3_ + _0.2_ = _7.5_

OVERALL QUALITY GRADE: 1 - 4 commercial, 4 - 6 good, (6 - 8 fine) 8 - 10 extra fine

scalloped cup tips

(Knotted,) ~~Continuous,~~ ___ ~~French wire,~~ ~~Bead tip,~~ ~~Clam shell tip,~~ (1500 to 2500)

CLASP: ___Oval spiral 14 x 18mm fishhook box clasp___
"750" and "*140 AR" on WG hook and YG box

pearls cost: __2911__ , clasp cost: __100__ , assembly cost: ⟶ _____ , total: __3011__

APPRAISER: ⓒ   >3312 >>6480 ~ $6500.00

Notes to the examples

These comments relate to the work sheets for the items in the example appraisal.

Item #1
- ring size is important identifying information
- a yellow gold item with white gold setting(s) is the usual combination of yellow and white gold, so I just circle them on the form. Any other combination of metals would be written on the *other* line with predominant metals first.
- rbc dia. Is just my shorthand for round brilliant cut diamond(s)
- when the standard formula for calculating stone weight has an adjustment applied, I always indicate that adjustment on the work sheet but I don't bother to write out the formula each time. 9.64 x 9.70 x 5.6 x 0.0061 x 0.98 was the calculation in this case
- the colour grade(s) recorded indicate a range because a mounted diamond cannot be graded as accurately as a loose stone. If a diamond is mounted in yellow gold, the "spread" of the reported range may be over three or four grades. The colour grade I use in pricing will always be the centre (or just above) of the recorded range. Sometimes, as in this example, the grade used in pricing is bolded by overprinting it
- in the $/ct line, 6700 is the $US list price in the Gemworld Price Guide, 0.73 is the exchange rate (at that time) for the Canadian dollar, and 9178 is the per carat cost rounded up to the next whole Canadian dollar
- the mount, grams net is calculated by deducting the weight of all stones from the weight of the item, 3.629 – (3.13/5) = 3.003 being the calculation here. In this and most cases the deduction has no significance in the calculation of value, but by standardizing the procedure to always calculate the net gram weight, I won't accidentally forget to do it when it is significant.
- 31.00 is the bullion value of the raw gold, arrived at by multiplying the mount grams net by 10.32 dollars per gram for fourteen Karat with gold at $550 per ounce
- multiplying by 1.4 adds 40% to cover both refining charges and the manufacturers mark-up on the metal
- plus 35 is the manufacturer's charges for casting, grinding, assembling, and finishing

- times 1.3 adds a 30% distributor's mark-up to this off-the-shelf type mount
- plus 13 is the hypothetical retailer's cost of setting the one stone
- times 1.1 adds a 10% hidden Excise Tax on the total cost. Although our hypothetical retailer would be paying that tax separately on each component, it is easier to do one calculation than to add 10% to each part of the cost. The arithmetic yields exactly the same answer in both ways of calculating
- to the tax-in cost I apply the appropriate mark-up formula from the fine jewellery mark-up schedule. (This differs from the schedule on page 124 because it reflects the schedule in use at that time). I have not rounded any of the numbers as I've gone along; I just leave them in the calculator, which means fewer keystrokes. My last calculation, then, was (31 726.24790192 − 20 000) x 1.34 + 29 800 which shows up on the calculator as 45 513.1721885728
- in rounding to retail, I'll round up or down according to how I feel about the case. In this case, I think the numbers are pushing the upper limit of retail, so I round down.

Item #2
- handmade means the piece was produced from flat stock and/or wire, rather than cast or assembled from standard findings
- 4-PY means the four-prong setting is in yellow gold, a bit unusual (except for emeralds), 4-PW means that four-prong white gold settings are on the sides
- I tend to list the stones in an item in the order of major to minor
- the number of stones in each category is circled to emphasize that it is the count (not an ordinal number)
- closer examination showed that the pavilion facets were not standard step cut but one row of step facets around a modified brilliant apex, not a named cut. For an important stone the cut could be described, but it must at least be stated that the stone is faceted
- the price guide which I used had separate listings for "golden/yellow topaz, sometimes referred to as precious topaz" and "imperial topaz" so I indicate which I used to price the stone. Because the word imperial is not a recognized variety name, I place it in quotation marks
- the topaz's colour is strong purity, medium tone, and orange-yellow hue. The quality number 6 comes from The Guide Reference Manual, Color Systems page 18 on the chart Topaz, Yellow to Red, yO, purity 5, tone 5 (see section starting p97)

- topaz is a type I stone so the clarity grade FI(VS1), according to the chart (p102) would be number 9 on a scale of 1 to 10
- vg means very good, of course, and the "make grades" chart (p104) sets this as 8 out of 10
- to get the overall quality grade, we consider the chart (p105). The starting colour of grade 6 is either the lowest of *fine 6 to 8* or the highest of *good 4 to 6* and in this case it doesn't matter which column I choose to work with because I end up with the same overall quality by either calculation. If I start with colour 6 as *fine 6 to 8* (rounding up as it were) then the influence of 9 clarity is an increase of 0.25 whilst influence of 8 make is an increase of 0.25 (using the 8 to 10 column rather than the 6 to 8 column, rounding up to balance the earlier rounding down) for the same 6.5 overall stone quality
- the range of list prices for fine (6 to 8) topaz over three carats in weight is 200 to 500, so the specific price for quality 6.5 is calculated by proportioning it within that range. The formula is 500 – 200 (to get the price spread) divided by two (to get the price difference for each full quality grade difference) multiplied by 0.5 (the amount by which the stone's quality is above the low end of this range) plus 200 (the price for the low end of this range), then the division by 0.73 is to convert to $ Canadian, and 373 is the per carat cost rounded up to the next whole Canadian dollar
- 2.4D in the *mm* line means 2.4 mm in diameter
- the diamonds are split-graded I-J, which coincides with the range of colour grades in one price group for diamonds of this size. If split grades straddle more than one price group, I use the price group that includes the centre (or just above[24] centre) grade within the stated range. In my rough notes I may bold the grade(s) that fall within the price group I used for valuing
- the dark room response of the left diamond (I set left and right with the metal quality stamping visible as upright) to ultraviolet light is nil while the right diamond shows very slight blue fluorescence. My notes always assume fluorescence response recorded is under long-wave ultraviolet. For the rarer short-wave ultraviolet fluorescence, I would specifically record the wavelength.
- the price guide I use assumes a good diamond make, so the very good

---

[24] A split grade of L-M-N-O, for example, would be priced at the colour M or the price group for stones with a colour range including the colour M, which for one case might be "K-L-M" and for a different case might be "M-N-O".

make of these two small diamonds requires a premium. The list price of 450 is divided by 0.73 to convert to $ Canadian, multiplied by 1.2 to add a 20% make premium, and 740 is the per carat cost rounded up to the next whole Canadian dollar.

o   the *mount grams net* is calculated as the total gram weight of the item less one fifth of the total carat weight (to convert carats to grams) of the stones. In figures this is (3.946 − (3.01 + 0.10)/5 = 3.324 but be sure to observe the brackets, otherwise the calculation will yield a meaningless number

o   34.30 is the bullion value of the raw gold, arrived at by multiplying the *mount grams net* by 10.32 dollars per gram for fourteen Karat with gold at $550 per ounce

o   multiplying by 1.4 adds 40% to cover both refining charges and the manufacturer's mark-up on the metal

o   plus 140 is the charges for designing and hand making the ring

o   because this is a handmade piece rather than an off-the-shelf type mount, a distributor's mark-up is not appropriate and so *x 1.3* is crossed out in the formula

o   plus 14.50 is the hypothetical retailer's cost of setting the three stones

o   the cost for the topaz (1134.77), diamonds (74.00), and mount and set (202.53) are added together for a total cost of 1411.30

o   times 1.1 adds in the 10% hidden Excise Tax for a tax-in cost of 1552.42

o   using the *fine jewellery* mark-up schedule for that time (which differed from the newer schedule on p124) this increased to 3 449.61 which rounds to $3 500.00 excluding retail taxes.

Item #3

o   the length is recorded to the nearest mm and to the nearest 1/4"

o   the gross weight of 34.1gm is not relevant to valuation, but is to item identification

o   the number of pearls, 46, is circled to emphasize that it is the count

o   the dimensions recorded are the *minimum* diameter of the smallest and the *minimum* diameter of the largest cultured pearl

o   information is circled and modifying adjectives added for each of the various qualities. Wherever 1 to 10 scale numbers are beside a quality, the chosen number is circled rather than the name of the quality that will be used in the description portion of the appraisal. Colour and overtone descriptions are indicated in the *colour* and the *overtones* columns with combined *colour/overtone quality* circled in the

Colour Grade (North American) block
- o the bonus for orient will not be decided until after all other qualities are proportioned toward the overall quality grade
  shape @ 15% is 10 x 0.15 = 1.5
  colour/overtones @ 10% is 7 x 0.10 = 0.7
  lustre @ 25% is 6 x 0.25 = 1.5
  complexion @ 20% is 7 x 0.20 = 1.4
  matching @ 5% is 4 x 0.05 = 0.2
  nacre thickness @ 25% is 8 x 0.25 = 2.0

this subtotals to 7.3 overall before addition of the orient bonus
- o the orient bonus is approximated as 10% of the balance toward overall 10 quality, which in calculation is (10 − 7.3) x 0.10 = 0.27. I generally apply only one decimal place (and ignore additional decimal place numerals), so I allowed 0.2 for the bonus
- o the overall quality grade, 7.3 + 0.2 = 7.5, falls in the *fine (6 to 8)* category, which the Gemworld Price Guide showed as having a price range of 1500 to 2500 American for an 18" necklace on a standard 14K clasp
- o the cup tips differ from bead tips in that a bead tip has a small hollow facing out to hold an end knot and a metal hook to attach, while a cup tip has a larger cup facing back to cup over the last pearl and attaches to the clasp with an "O" ring
- o clasp dimensions are to the nearest millimetre, and markings are drawn within quotation marks as they appear
- o the price of the pearls is calculated from the range of prices for the size and quality, considering the necklace length and currency conversion. In this case, the formula was
  ((2500 − 1500)/2 x 1.5 + 1500) x 17/18/0.73 = 2910.95890411, which is 2911 at the next highest Canadian dollar.
  2500 − 1500 gives the price spread across the *(6 to 8) fine* grades
  dividing by two gives the price spread for each full overall quality grade step
  x 1.5 is the quality difference of this strand above minimum quality of the range
  1500 is the price of the minimum quality in this range
  17/18 is the length of this necklace divided by the length of the necklace for which this price list gives quotes
  and finally, dividing by 0.73 converted from American to Canadian dollars
- o 100 Canadian is allowed for the upgrade from a standard 14K clasp to the larger 18K clasp with end cups
- o the total cost is then 3011 before taxes
- o multiplying by 1.1 adds in the 10% hidden Excise Tax
- o and my *standard jewellery* mark-up brought this up to 6480
- o which rounds to $6 500.00 retail, excluding retail sales taxes.

Diamond weight

Rough ....(octahedron crystal) ....(average W)^3 x 0.00829 = ct

Round ....(brilliant)...........minimum W x maximum W x D x 0.0061 = ct

....................(old European) ....as brilliant + 5 (to 15)% = ct

....................(rose cut) ....W x W x D x (0.0050 to 0.0053) = ct

Oval ....(brilliant)...............................L x W x D x 0.0062 = ct

....................(old European)..........................as brilliant + 5(to 15)% = ct

Old mine cut ....average W x average diagonal x D x 0.0067 = ct

Rectangle ....(Barion) ....L x W x D x 0.0082 = ct

....................(Princess) ....L x W x D x 0.0083 = ct

....................(emerald cut @ L/W=1.0) ....L x W x D x 0.008 = ct

....................(emerald cut @ L/W=1.5) ....L x W x D x 0.0092 = ct

....................(emerald cut @ L/W=2.0) ....L x W x D x 0.010 = ct

....................(emerald cut @ L/W=2.5) ....L x W x D x 0.0106 = ct

Pear shape ......(brilliant @ L/W=1.25) ....L x W x D x 0.00615 = ct

....................(@ L/W=1.5) ....L x W x D x 0.0060 = ct

....................(@ L/W=1.66) ....L x W x D x 0.0059 = ct

....................(@ L/W=2.0) ....L x W x D x 0.00575 = ct

Marquise ....(brilliant @ L/W=1.5) ....L x W x D x 0.00565 = ct

....................(@ L/W=2.0) ....L x W x D x 0.0058 = ct

....................(@ L/W=2.5) ....L x W x D x 0.00585 = ct

....................(@ L/W=3.0) ....L x W x D x 0.00595 = ct

Triangle............(Trilliant, Trillion) ....A x B x D x 0.0057 = ct

....................(cut corner step cut) ....A x B x D x 0.0051 = ct

Heart shape (brilliant) ....H x W x D x 0.0059 = ct

A = altitude, B = base, D = depth, L = length, W = width,

Coloured stone weight

FACETED STONE FORMULAE:

Round mixed cut; ....W x W x D x SG x 0.0020 = ct

Round brilliant cut; ....W x W x D x SG x 0.00173= ct

Oval mixed cut; ....(well cut) ....L x W x D x SG x 0.0022 = ct

(very shallow)........L x W x D x SG x 0.0027 = ct

Octagonal step cut: ....("square") ....W x W x D x SG x 0.0023 = ct

("rectangle").........L x W x D x SG x 0.0026 = ct

Marquise mixed cut; ....L x W x D x SG x 0.0017 = ct

Pear shape mixed cut; ....L x W x D x SG x 0.0018 = ct

CABOCHON STONE FORMULAE:

Round cabochon;   (high) ....W x W x D x SG x 0.0021 = ct

(low) ....W x W x D x SG x 0.0024 = ct

(buff top) ....W x W x D x SG x 0.0027 = ct

Oval cabochon; ....(high) ....L x W x D x SG x 0.0023 = ct

(low) ....L x W x D x SG x 0.0026 = ct

(buff top) ....L x W x D x SG x 0.0029 = ct

Octagonal square cabochon; ....(high) ....W x W x D x SG x 0.0025 = ct

(low) ....W x W x D x SG x 0.00275= ct

(buff top) ....W x W x D x SG x 0.0031 = ct

Octagonal rectangular cabochon; (high) ....L x W x D x SG x 0.00285= ct

(low) ....L x W x D x SG x 0.0031 = ct

(buff top) ....L x W x D x SG x 0.0035 = ct

Marquise cabochon; ....use faceted formula: + 10% if high,   + 20% if low

Pear cabochon; ....use faceted formula: + 10% if high,   + 20% if low

Ball; ....(deduct up to 5% for hole)W x W x W x SG x 0.00262 = ct

D = depth, L = length, W = width, SG = specific gravity

Standard stone sizes

Rounds:
From 2 mm in increasing increments of 0.25 mm up to 7 mm, then in increasing increments of 0.5 mm up to 15 mm.

Ovals:

80 x 50	60 x 32	50 x 35	50 x 25	45 x 30	40 x 30	40 x 18
38 x 27	38 x 25	35 x 18	35 x 13	34 x 22	32 x 15	30 x 24
30 x 20	30 x 15	28 x 10	28 x 8	26 x 12	25 x 19	25 x 18
25 x 15	24 x 14	24 x 13	24 x 10	22 x 16	22 x 10	22 x 8
20 x 14	20 x 12	20 x 10	20 x 5	18 x 13	18 x 12	18 x 10
18 x 9	16 x 14	16 x 12	16 x 9	16 x 8	15 x 10	14 x 12
14 x 10	14 x 9	14 x 8	12 x 10	11 x 9	10 x 8	10 x 6
9 x 7	8 x 6.5	8 x 6	7 x 5	6 x 4	5 x 3	3 x 2

Rectangle, Octagon, Antique cushion:

18 x 13	16 x 14	16 x 12	16 x 9	16 x 8
15 x 11	14 x 12	14 x 10	13 x 8	12 x 10
12 x 8	10 x 8	8 x 6	6 x 4	

Pear shape:

15 x 10	14.5 x 8.5	14 x 9	13 x 8	12 x 8
10 x 7	9 x 6	8 x 6	8 x 5	7 x 5
6 x 4	5 x 3			

Marquise (Navette):

20 x 10	18 x 9	16 x 8	15 x 7	12 x 6
10 x 5	8 x 4	6 x 3	4 x 2	

Stone Size (ss)/Pearl Plate (pp) approximate size comparison to millimetres

SS	1	2	3	4	5	6	7	8	9	10	11
PP	4-5	6-7	8-9	10	11-12	13-14	15-16	17-18	19-20	21	22-23
mm	1	1⅛	1¼	1½	1¾	2	2⅛	2¼	2½	2¾	3

SS	12	13	14	15	16	17	18	19	20	21	22
PP	24-25	26	27	28-29	30	31-32	33	34	35	36-37	38-39
mm	3⅛	3¼	3⅜	3½	3¾	4	4⅛	4¼	4⅜	4½	4¾

SS	23	24	25	26	27	28	29	30	31	32	33
PP	40	41-42	43-44	45-46	--	--	--	--	--	--	--
mm	5	5¼	5⅜	5½	5¾	6	6⅛	6¼	6½	6¾	6⅞

SS	34	35	36	37	38	39	40	41	42	43	44
mm	7	7¼	7½	7¾	8	8¼	8½	8¾	9	9½	10

SS	45	46	47	48	49	50
mm	10¼	10½	11	11½	11¾	12

Mêlée diamonds, approximate number of stones per carat

Brilliant cut stones:

mm >	3.0	2.9	2.8	2.7	2.6	2.5	2.4	2.3	2.2	2.1	2.0	1.9	1.8	1.7	1.6	1.5	1.4
#/ct >	**10**	**11**	**12**	**14**	**16**	**18**	**20**	**22**	**25**	**29**	**33**	**37**	**43**	**50**	**59**	**71**	**87**

Single cut stones:

mm>	2.3	2.2	2.1	2.0	1.9	1.8	1.7	1.6	1.5	1.4	1.3	1.2	1.1	1.0	0.9
#/ct>	**21**	**23**	**26**	**30**	**34**	**40**	**48**	**57**	**69**	**85**	**102**	**126**	**157**	**200**	**243**

Weight conversions

Units	carat	gram	DWT	Troy oz.	grain	Avoir. oz.
1 Avoirdupois lb	2267.96185	453.59237	291.66666	14.5833	7000	16
1 Troy lb	1866.20861	373.2417216	240	12	5760	13.16571
1 Troy oz	155.517384	31.1034768	20	1	480	1.0971429
1 Avoirdupois oz	141.7476	528.349523	18.22916	0.9114583	437.5	1
1 Pennyweight	7.77587	1.555174	1	0.05	24	0.05486
1 Gram	5	1	0.6430149	0.032150746	15.432358	0.03527396

Special appraisal report

Seymour Proffet, Partner,   July 12th, 1996
   Havelok Smyth
   Victoria Plumbe,
KLMN Chartered Accountants,
Suite 16, 1 Prudent Path,
Megalopolis, Canada. B4U 0R8

Dear Mr. Proffet:

On Friday June 28th 1996, by request of Mr. Havelok Smyth in a telephone conversation Thursday May 30th, I attended at the premises of Alpha And Omega Jewellery Manufacturing Limited, 2001 Production Place, Megalopolis, Canada, for a physical inventory count with KLMN representative Ms. Victoria Plumbe.

Please find enclosed with this letter of transmittal my report regarding α & ω and my invoice.

In "Box #4" the stones called *pearl* are neither natural nor cultured pearl but are cut mother-of-pearl, the stones called *spinel* are colourless synthetic spinel, and the purported *onyx* are neither natural nor dyed onyx (with layers of black/white) but are rather the black dyed chalcedony called black onyx. Considering the small values allowed for these items, these appear to be nomenclature errors rather than any attempt at misrepresentation. The damaged "miscellaneous stones" contained in "Box #3" should be written off as valueless.

Yours truly,

Richard H. Cartier, FGA, FCGmA

RHC/swv   encl.

GEMMOLOGIST'S REPORT

Alpha And Omega Jewellery Manufacturing Limited

Annual Inventory Count
June 28th, 1996

by

Richard H. Cartier, FGA, FCGmA

#1 Valuation Way, Megalopolis, Canada. O2B 4U2

Table of Contents

The purpose of this report is to confirm or establish identification and value of samples of the annual inventory of Alpha And Omega Jewellery Manufacturing Limited as of June 30th 1996.

On Friday June 28th 1996, I attended at the premises of Alpha And Omega Jewellery Limited, 2001 Production Place, Megalopolis Canada, for a physical inventory count with KLMN General Accountant's representative Ms. Victoria Plumbe.

I selected items for identification/quality/value check from photocopies of the inventory listed on sheets entitled *Alpha And Omega Jewellery Manufacturing Limited* stamped "063096" numbers 1 through 20; sheets entitled *PRODUCTION CONTROL CASTING/RING DEPT.* numbered 21 through 24 dated JUNE 27/96; sheets entitled *PRODUCTION CONTROL ASSEMBLY DEPT.* numbered 25 and 26 dated JUNE 27/96; and computer generated sheets entitled *Item Valuation Report – LOOSE STONES* pages 1 through 11 dated "Jun 28 96 7:47am".

I carried out an examination (within the limits of on-site examination outside the controlled environment of a fully equipped gemmology laboratory) of the items listed in the annexed schedule A, which has been initialled by me for the purpose of identification. The values appended to each item are one or more of:

Scrap value: the perceived minimum amount that should reasonably be expected when seeking to convert the entire lot into immediate cash. It considers bullion value minus an allowance for refining, and excludes all taxes.

Bullion value: the perceived value of the pure gold content in the entire lot according to international exchanges as of the valuation date, excluding all taxes.

Refined value: the perceived value of the entire lot incorporating bullion value with an allowance for refining, including Excise Tax and excluding GST.

Bulk value: the perceived value of the entire lot as might be realized in the wholesaling of greater than minimum-order-requirement volumes, including Excise Tax and excluding GST

Wholesale value: (loose stones & findings) the perceived value per unit weight as might be charged to a small volume purchaser for all or any portion of the lot, including excise Tax and excluding GST.

Each value: (finished goods) the perceived value of each pair of items or of each single item (as appropriate) in the lot at wholesale as might be charged to a small volume purchaser, including Excise Tax and excluding GST.

In verifying the accuracy of the weigh scales used on site for the count, I found all scales showed less than 0.05% disagreement with my electronic scale and with my analytical scale with one exception. The very large Setra model 12000L scale in the large vault had a small mass reading that was 0.25% light.

I selected the samples I examined on a random basis from the chosen lots, with slight concentration on the more sizeable or valuable lots. I did not necessarily verify counts or total weights but examined, graded, weighed and performed electrochemical or touchstone tests on metal parts of a sample from each of the lots in the annexed schedule A. Standard gem identification techniques were used to identify the gemstones including refractive index measurement, spectroscopic analysis, microscopic examination, thermal conductivity meter, and other gemmological equipment.

Insofar as items were identified, all tests confirmed the purported gem identification and/or the purported metal qualities, except for the three lots referred to in the following paragraph. Weights of loose stones are reported to two decimal places according to an electronic analytical scale giving repeatable weights to 0.001 carat, with the third decimal place ignored unless it is a nine, in which case the second decimal is rounded up. Weights of mounted stones are estimated from physical dimensions and assumed specific gravities. Measurements of mounted stones are by bench micrometer, Leveridge gauge, or table gauge (in descending order of accuracy) according to the accessibility of each stone to the measuring devices, with more accurate devices implemented wherever possible. The carat weights of all loose gemstones examined agreed with the weights marked on their packaging within 0.01 carat, but I did not confirm the final tally of counts, weights, and value against the full inventory count.

In "Box #4" the stones called *pearl* (stones p.9 lines 8 to 11) are neither natural nor cultured pearl but are cut mother-of-pearl, the stones called *spinel* (stones p.10 lines 14 to 20) are colourless synthetic spinel, and the purported *onyx* (stones p. 11 lines 5 to 14) are neither natural nor dyed onyx (with layers of black/white) but are rather the black dyed chalcedony called "black onyx". Considering the small stated values, this appears to be nomenclature errors rather than any attempt at misrepresentation. The damaged "miscellaneous stones" contained in "Box #3" (stones p.11 line 26) seemed over-valued considering that the 11 x 9 mm opal is very crazed and the other stones in that lot are either chipped or broken. It would appear that these stones are listed in the inventory at their cost, which may not seem entirely unreasonable, but it would be more realistic to write them off as valueless.

The June 30th values are based on gold at US $382.00 per ounce, the Canadian dollar at US $0.7336 as reported on the front page of the business section of the Globe And Mail newspaper on Friday June 28th 1996, and gemstone prices as reported in Gemworld Price Guide at the end of June. Values are rounded to the nearest $5, $25, $100, or $1 000 according to whether above or below the thresholds of $200, $2 000, or $50 000. Values below $50 are rounded up to the next fifty cents.

CONCLUSIONS

It is my considered opinion that the goods and materials that I examined on June 28th 1996 from the inventory count of Alpha And Omega Jewellery Manufacturing Limited showed a few nomenclature errors but were otherwise correctly described in all material respects.

Richard H. Cartier, FGA, FCGmA

APPRAISER'S CERTIFICATE

This is to certify that:

I, Richard H. Cartier, have no interest in Alpha And Omega Jewellery Manufacturing Limited or in the metals, gemstones, or jewellery evaluated in this report.

I have personally inspected every article described in this report and, to the best of my knowledge and belief, the annexed schedule A is, in all material respects, an accurate record of the items examined by me.

Neither my commission to perform this examination and produce the report nor my fee for professional services is contingent upon the level of my estimate of value.

date: July 12th 1996

signature: *R Cartier*

Richard H. Cartier, FGA, FCGmA

WEIGHING A MOUNTED STONE HYDROSTATICALLY
(or hydrostatically testing SG of the metal part of jewellery)

I'm not sure where I encountered the idea; I think it was either through the Journal of Gemmology or in the Gem & Jewellery News, both from the Gemmological Association and Gem Testing Laboratory of Great Britain, the second also being the quarterly bulletin of the Society of Jewellery Historians.

I remember that the explanation of why the formula would work didn't convince me, but I was taken with the idea of hydrostatically weighing a mounted stone or calculating the specific gravity of the metal in an item of jewellery, so I played with a series of equations until I convinced myself the formulas were logical.

First I'll explain the legends I used, and then show my formula derivation. Please, if you're bored to tears by the thought of formula derivation just skip over this bit and go straight to the formulae themselves.

Symbol legend	Subscript legend
A = weight in air	$_m$ = of the original specified metal
G = specific gravity	$_s$ = of the original specified stone(s)
L = loss of weight in water	$_t$ = of the total <u>article</u>
H = hypothetical weight in air of an identical size and shape article having a uniform single composition	$_d$ = of the diamond(s) only

$G = A/L$ ... so [1] $L = A/G$ ... and [2] $A = LG$, ... and then [3] $H = LG$

[4] $A_m = L_mG_m$ ... and [5] $A_s = L_sG_s$

[6] $A_t = A_m + A_s$ (total weight = sum of weight of parts)

so ... [7] $A_t = L_mG_m + L_sG_s$ (by substituting from [4] & [5] to [6])

By extrapolating from [3] through [7] to a hypothetical object identical in shape and size composed entirely of metal (having the same volume), we get...

[8] $H_m = L_mG_m + L_sG_m$ (*The weight of the hypothetical all-metal object will equal (the loss in weight by that portion of the shape that was originally metal multiplied by the specific gravity of the metal) added to (the loss in weight of that portion of the shape that was originally stone multiplied by the specific gravity of the metal).*) so then, with [7]...

[9] $H_m - A_t = (L_mG_m + L_sG_m) - (L_mG_m + L_sG_s)$ which becomes...

[10] $H_m - A_t = L_mG_m + L_sG_m - L_mG_m - L_sG_s$ which simplifies to...

[11] $H_m - A_t = L_sG_m - L_sG_s$ which becomes...

[12] $H_m - A_t = L_s(G_m - G_s)$ then divide both sides by $G_m - G_s$

[13] $(H_m - A_t)/(G_m - G_s) = L_s$ now multiply both sides by G_s

[14] $G_s(H_m - A_t)/(G_m - G_s) = L_sG_s$ now, for L_sG_s substitute A_s from [5]

[15] $G_s(H_m - A_t)/(G_m - G_s) = A_s$ which reverses to...

[16] $A_s = G_s(H_m - A_t)/(G_m - G_s)$ now replace H_m with L_tG_m from [3] giving...

The weight of a mounted stone...

[17] $A_s = G_s(L_tG_m - A_t)/(G_m - G_s)$ to calculate the weight of a mounted stone in a solitaire ring or a group of the same stones mounted in a cluster. Just keep in mind the units of weight you are using!

For an article containing diamonds as well as coloured stones, calculation of the carat weight of diamonds from standard formulae is relatively accurate, so one can modify the above formula to deduct the weight of diamonds at each step and still hydrostatically estimate the weight of a centre coloured stone with the following formula...

The weight of mounted stones (while deducting diamond weight)...

[18] $A_s = G_s(A_d+(L_t-A_d/G_d)G_m-A_t)/(G_m - G_s)$

I recommend that you do all the weighing in carats. If you are weighing in grams you'll need to remember to divide the calculated carat weight of the diamond(s) by five to convert to grams and also multiply the final answer by five to convert the stone weight into carats.

The similar formula you can use to calculate the specific gravity of the metal portion of the article when the weight and specific gravity of the stone are known or surmised is...

Specific Gravity of metal...

[19] $G_m = (A_t-A_s)/(L_t-A_s/G_s)$

Specific gravities of some pure metals are:
Gold 19.32;   Platinum 21.45;   Iridium 22.65;   Palladium 12.02;
    Ruthenium 12.45;   Rhodium 12.41;   Silver 10.49

Typical specific gravities of some alloys are:
10K yellow 11.56, white 11.09;   14K yellow 13.07, white 12.61;
18K yellow 15.58, white 14.64;   10% Irid-Plat 21.56;
5% Ru-Plat 20.70;   Sterling 10.40;   Coin silver 10.35

Styles of cut

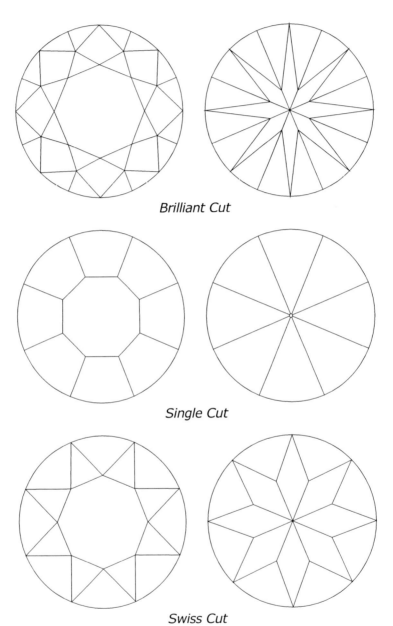

Brilliant Cut

Single Cut

Swiss Cut

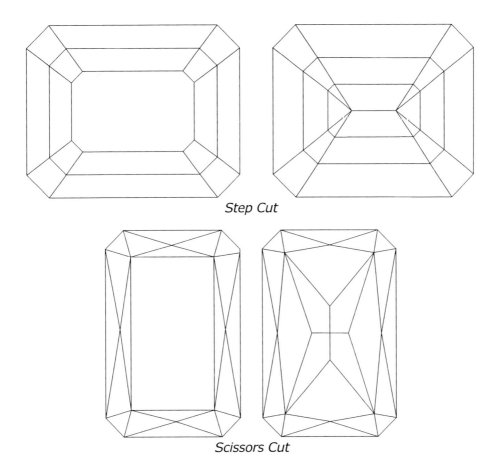

Step Cut

Scissors Cut

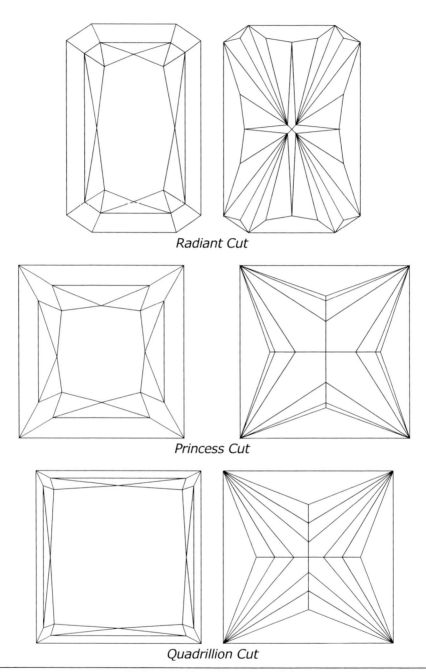

Radiant Cut

Princess Cut

Quadrillion Cut

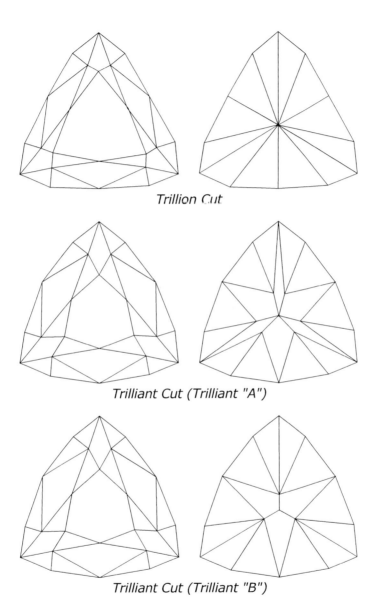

Trillion Cut

Trilliant Cut (Trilliant "A")

Trilliant Cut (Trilliant "B")

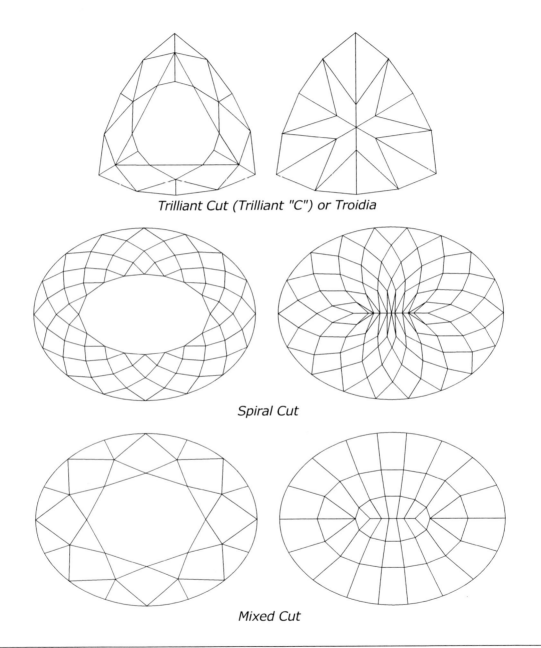

Trilliant Cut (Trilliant "C") or Troidia

Spiral Cut

Mixed Cut

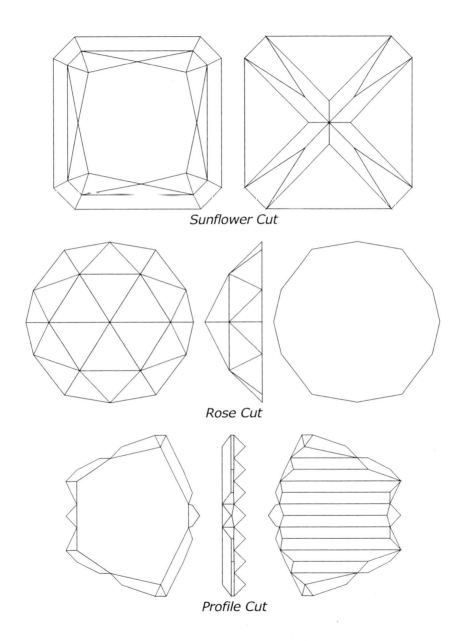

Sunflower Cut

Rose Cut

Profile Cut

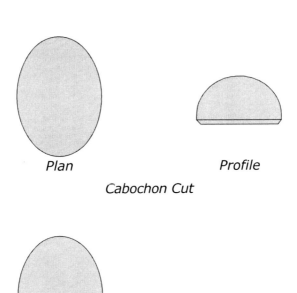

Plan   *Profile*

Cabochon Cut

Plan   *Profile*

Buff Top Cabochon Cut

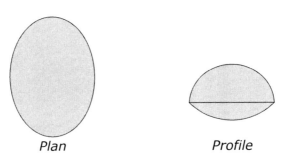

Plan   *Profile*

Double Cabochon Cut

Gemstone shapes

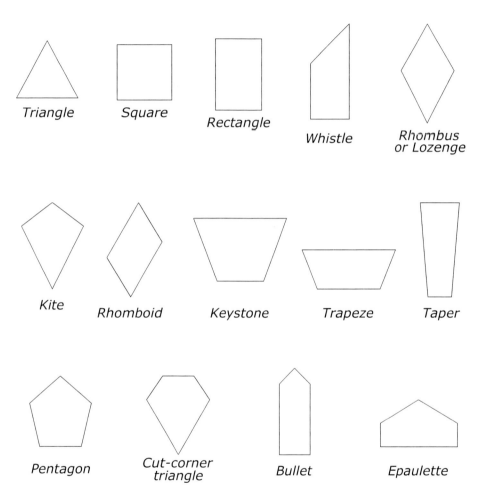

Triangle · Square · Rectangle · Whistle · Rhombus or Lozenge

Kite · Rhomboid · Keystone · Trapeze · Taper

Pentagon · Cut-corner triangle · Bullet · Epaulette

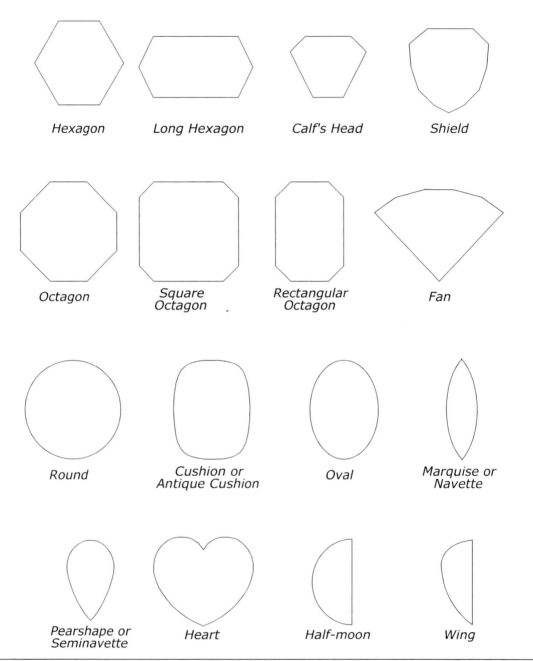

Hexagon   Long Hexagon   Calf's Head   Shield

Octagon   Square Octagon   Rectangular Octagon   Fan

Round   Cushion or Antique Cushion   Oval   Marquise or Navette

Pearshape or Seminavette   Heart   Half-moon   Wing

Chain styles

Cable

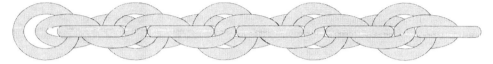

Rope or Double Cable

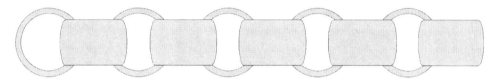

Belcher or Rolo

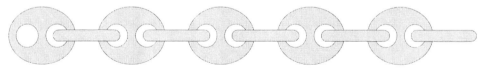

Gucci

Anchor or Marine

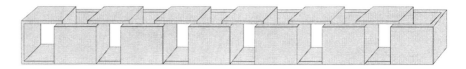

Venetian Box

Crinkle

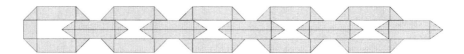

Boston

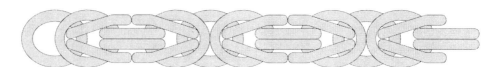

Byzantine or King

Foxtail

Figaro

Curb

Double Curb

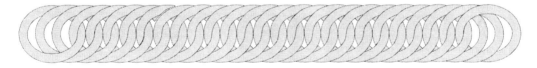

Triple Curb

Twisted Double Curb or Singapore

Espiga or Wheat

Banana or "C"-Link

Bismarck

Cuban Link

Herringbone (single)

Herringbone

Herringbone (triple)

Herringbone (quad)

Serpentine

Scroll

Cobra

Figure Eight

Turkish (Leaf Design)

Snake

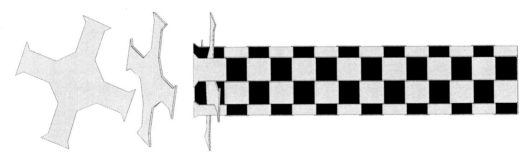

Popcorn

Index